# MATHS

## FOR PRACTICE & REVISION

# 1

DECIMALS

FRACTIONS

PERCENTAGE

## PETER ROBSON

### Newby Books

PO BOX 40, SCARBOROUGH
NORTH YORKSHIRE, YO12 5TW

**DECIMAL COLUMNS**

Learn the names of the columns

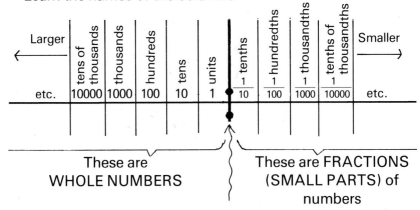

These are
WHOLE NUMBERS

These are FRACTIONS
(SMALL PARTS) of
numbers

This is the
DECIMAL POINT

---

 **Writing decimal numbers**

*Always look for the POINT. This tells you in which columns to put the numbers.

*The UNITS (ones) column is always just to the LEFT of the point.

e.g. (1)   37.450

---

e.g. (2)   0.0728

---

 If you cannot see a point, the last figure is in the UNITS column

e.g.   629

## a

Draw decimal columns down your page

etc.

and write each of these numbers in the correct columns.
Always look first for the POINT or the UNITS column.

| | | | |
|---|---|---|---|
| 1) 32.86 | 5) 0.671 | 9) 86.5 | 13) 15 |
| 2) 1.507 | 6) 500.3 | 10) 4.8821 | 14) 23.056 |
| 3) 924.2 | 7) 1.012 | 11) 0.7 | 15) 0.008 |
| 4) 511.85 | 8) 970 | 12) 362.98 | |

## b

Copy these numbers, and in each number underline the figure
which is in the UNITS column

e.g.   428.95 = 428.95

| | | | |
|---|---|---|---|
| 1) 59.8 | 5) 4624.5 | 9) 5.82 | 13) 0.0042 |
| 2) 6.510 | 6) 3.9785 | 10) 113.07 | 14) 60.0 |
| 3) 322.7 | 7) 7100 | 11) 6 | 15) 0.1 |
| 4) 1.4 | 8) 0.052 | 12) 739.135 | |

## c

Draw decimal columns and write these numbers correctly.
For each of the numbers give the NAME of the column which
has a figure 4, e.g.

30.42    | | 3 | 0 | 4 | 2 | |    4 is in the TENTHS column

| | | | |
|---|---|---|---|
| 1) 14.3 | 4) 174 | 7) 0.401 | 9) 4990 |
| 2) 548.5 | 5) 0.346 | 8) 47.8 | 10) 5.324 |
| 3) 9.4 | 6) 428.5 | | |

## d

Copy these numbers, and for each number give the name of the
column which has a figure 7

| | | | |
|---|---|---|---|
| 1) 372.5 | 4) 3.447 | 7) 0.788 | 9) 4733 |
| 2) 17.32 | 5) 7 | 8) 7654.0 | 10) 71.5 |
| 3) 66.175 | 6) 5.78 | | |

# A ✚ ADDITION

e.g. (1) 5.78 + 4 + 16.5

*1) Make quite sure you know
where the POINT is
in each number

5.78 + 4.0 + 16.5

**REMEMBER**   8  is   8.0
23  is   23.0
6  is   6.0, etc

*2) Write a row of points
one underneath the other

*3) Fit numbers carefully
in correct columns

```
   5.78
   4.0
+ 16.5
```

*4) Add, being sure to put
the point in your answer

```
   5.78
   4.0
+ 16.5
  26.28
```

---

e.g. (2)  14.64 + 7.2 + 5.125 + 12

```
  14.64
   7.2
   5.125
+ 12.0
  38.965
```

**a**

Make these numbers look more like decimals
(e.g.   7 = 7.0,   13 = 13.0)

| | | | |
|---|---|---|---|
| 1) 8 | 6) 32 | 11) 14 | 16) 67 |
| 2) 24 | 7) 1 | 12) 53 | 17) 312 |
| 3) 16 | 8) 125 | 13) 2 | 18) 18 |
| 4) 5 | 9) 6 | 14) 42 | 19) 650 |
| 5) 9 | 10) 47 | 15) 3000 | 20) 111 |

---

**b**

Try these additions

| | |
|---|---|
| 1) 6.2 + 5.6 | 6) 6.8 + 2.93 + 11.15 |
| 2) 12.5 + 7.8 | 7) 3.75 + 9.4 + 1.06 |
| 3) 3.9 + 5.3 | 8) 65.07 + 24.5 + 1.25 |
| 4) 5.28 + 9.76 | 9) 7.49 + 14 + 3.8 |
| 5) 4.3 + 6.28 | 10) 32 + 14.5 + 6.75 |

---

**c**

Find the SUM (adding) of each of these groups of numbers

| | |
|---|---|
| 1) 25.85, 6.66, 3.2 | 6) 9.68, 3.71, 12.9 |
| 2) 53, 8.2, 0.8 | 7) 75.2, 6.84, 0.325 |
| 3) 5.4, 3.2, 7.8, 0.3 | 8) 184, 36.9, 20.5 |
| 4) 6.72, 12.8, 2.17 | 9) 0.3, 0.0075, 0.014 |
| 5) 17, 12.6, 4.58 | 10) 8.85, 85, 5.585 |

---

**d**

Find the sum of each of these groups

| | |
|---|---|
| 1) 4.235, 0.52, 8.475 | 6) 99.9, 999, 9.99 |
| 2) 1350, 75.5, 623.25 | 7) 1.27, 3.49, 12.85, 3.2 |
| 3) 0.007, 0.083, 0.129 | 8) 87.55, 5.235, 119 |
| 4) 4.03, 0.084, 19.1 | 9) 0.00082, 0.0064, 0.0001 |
| 5) 27, 14.95, 8 | 10) 6.2, 34.8, 7.5, 1.15 |

# A ▬ SUBTRACTION

e.g. (1)   6 — 1.84

*1) Make quite sure you know
where the POINT is in each
number

**REMEMBER**   12   is   12.0
5   is   5.0
etc.

6.**0** — 1.84

*2) Write a row of points
one underneath the other

.
———·———
.

*3) Fit numbers carefully
in correct columns

6.0
— 1.84
———·———

*4) FILL IN ANY SPACES
WITH NOUGHTS

6.0**0**
— 1.84
———·———

*5) Subtract (take away),
being sure to put the point
in your answer

6.00
— 1.84
———
4.16

---

e.g. (2) Subtract 3.52 from 12.7

12.7**0**
— 3.52
———
9.18

The number you are subtracting
always goes at the bottom.

**a** Make these numbers look more like decimals
(e.g.   24 = 24.0,   8 = 8.0)

| | | | | |
|---|---|---|---|---|
| 1) 3 | 3) 62 | 5) 413 | 7) 5 | 9) 1000 |
| 2) 74 | 4) 9 | 6) 14 | 8) 87 | 10) 28 |

---

**b**

| | | |
|---|---|---|
| 1) 8.7 − 4.2 | 6) 14.2 − 7.8 | 11) 17.51 − 4.9 |
| 2) 16.3 − 11.1 | 7) 0.37 − 0.29 | 12) 0.012 − 0.005 |
| 3) 9.6 − 6.1 | 8) 5.38 − 3.64 | 13) 8.25 − 5 |
| 4) 25.8 − 14.8 | 9) 21.3 − 2.8 | 14) 3.805 − 1.062 |
| 5) 7.6 − 2.3 | 10) 6.23 − 1.8 | 15) 20.0 − 3.8 |

---

**c** Remember to fill in spaces with noughts if necessary

| | | |
|---|---|---|
| 1) 15.2 − 8.4 | 6) 6.19 − 6.045 | 11) 62 − 14.32 |
| 2) 4.3 − 1.9 | 7) 9.07 − 7.8 | 12) 5.482 − 3.917 |
| 3) 6.7 − 1.46 | 8) 42.5 − 7.36 | 13) 22.2 − 4.56 |
| 4) 32.45 − 15.7 | 9) 0.306 − 0.04 | 14) 10.03 − 8.8 |
| 5) 28 − 4.6 | 10) 1.5 − 0.75 | 15) 0.9 − 0.07 |

---

**d**

1) 34.5 − 22.2

2) 6.27 − 4.8

3) 0.325 − 0.29

4) 9.50 − 1.77

5) 40 − 12.5

6) 1.35 − 1.275

7) 6.28 − 0.08

8) 53.1 − 7.63

9) 0.0006 − 0.00002

10) 20 − 14.28

11) From 8.3 subtract 1.7

12) From 13.13 subtract 1.313

13) From 94 subtract 4.9

14) From 5.32 subtract 0.48

15) Find the difference between 18.1 and 2.7

16) Find the difference between 0.03 and 0.011

17) Find the difference between 47.5 and 38.0

18) Subtract 3.47 from 11.08

19) Subtract 0.99 from 1

20) Subtract 3.55 from 22.3

# A ➕ ➖ ADDITION & SUBTRACTION

e.g.  9.8 + 3.6 − 4.72

*Do each part SEPARATELY
(unless all the signs are + )

```
              9.8
        +     3.6
              13.4
Then          13.40
        −     4.72
              8.68
```

e.g. (2)

24 − 5.87 − 3.5

```
        24.00
      −  5.87
        18.13
      −  3.5
        14.63
```

e.g. (3)

62.5 − 46.9 + 25.4

```
      62.5        or      62.5
    − 46.9              + 25.4
      15.6                87.9
    + 25.4              − 46.9
      41.0                41.0
```

## B Brackets

e.g.  15.43 − (2.97 + 3.58)

*1) Always do the parts
   INSIDE the brackets first

```
          2.97
      +   3.58
          6.55
```

*2) Then do the other parts

```
        15.43
      −  6.55
         8.88
```

**a**

| 1) 5.62 + 2.17 | 6) 3.258 + 0.07 | 11) 27.5 + 27.5 |
| 2) 32.6 − 12.2 | 7) 15 − 9.73 | 12) 8.27 + 6 + 7.8 |
| 3) 1.43 + 18.8 | 8) 88.8 + 8.888 | 13) 14.22 − 5.075 |
| 4) 6 + 2.3 + 5.9 | 9) 6.7 − 2.14 | 14) 0.94 + 0.094 |
| 5) 30.2 − 19.3 | 10) 2 − 0.003 | 15) 100 − 82.3 |

**b**

| 1) 6.4 + 2.3 − 5.2 | 6) 2.9 + 5.5 − 8.3 |
| 2) 27 + 4.9 − 16.7 | 7) 7.8 − 2.1 − 3.4 |
| 3) 0.32 + 0.57 − 0.48 | 8) 50.5 − 23.6 + 8.4 |
| 4) 9.8 + 3.9 − 7.8 | 9) 0.911 + 0.747 + 0.208 |
| 5) 56.1 + 43.9 − 80.0 | 10) 1.7 + 5.6 − 4.25 |

**c**

If there are brackets, remember to do the part in brackets first

| 1) 4.32 + 3.57 − 5.46 | 6) (7.4 + 14.1) − (17.9 + 1.8) |
| 2) 16.9 − (10.5 + 4.1) | 7) 9.03 − 2.75 − 1.96 |
| 3) 0.372 + 0.088 − 0.163 | 8) 46 − (13.6 + 23.7) |
| 4) 9.43 − (2.17 + 5.34) | 9) 0.292 + 0.545 − 0.837 |
| 5) 3.785 + 6.87 + 9.345 | 10) 9.8 − (3 + 1.9 + 4.65) |

**d**

1) Add 18.5 to 16.9 and subtract 20.7
2) From the sum of 0.58 and 2.9 subtract 3
3) From 7.4 subtract the sum of 3.7 and 2.9
4) Add 1.006 to 2.013 and subtract 0.92 from the result
5) Subtract the sum of 25.9 and 17.8 from 50
6) From the sum of 1.05, 2.6 and 0.87, subtract 4.015
7) Subtract 4.9 from the sum of 3.08 and 2.97
8) From 7 subtract 1.7 and then subtract 0.17
9) Subtract the sum of 6.4 and 2.5 from the sum of 7.8 and 5.6
10) Find the difference between 7.6 and the sum of 3.2 and 8.2

# 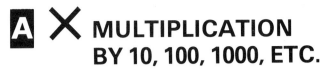 ✕ MULTIPLICATION BY 10, 100, 1000, ETC.

**NOTICE** that the **POINT DOES NOT MOVE** and the **FIGURES STAY THE SAME** (except for an extra nought now and then)

---

**B** **MULTIPLY BY 10**
\*Move the number
   ONE PLACE LARGER

e.g     2.378 × 10
      23.78

e.g.     4.03 × 10
     40.3

---

 **MULTIPLY BY 100**
\*Move the number
   TWO PLACES LARGER

e.g.     5.194 × 100
     519.4

e.g.     16.7 × 100
     167**0**

**REMEMBER** — Fill up to the point with noughts

---

**D** **MULTIPLY BY 1000**
\*Move the number
   THREE PLACES LARGER

e.g.     0.2437 × 1000
     243.7

e.g.     5.4 × 1000
   54**00**

**REMEMBER** — Fill up to the point with noughts

---

 (1) It is better to write 0.34 than .34
     The nought helps to show where the point is.
(2) How would you multiply by 10000 or 100000?

# a

Write these numbers and then multiply each of them by 10

| | | | |
|---|---|---|---|
| 1) 1.35 | 6) 0.395 | 11) 37.55 | 16) 4618.5 |
| 2) 29.78 | 7) 67.14 | 12) 4.683 | 17) 0.032 |
| 3) 4.657 | 8) 1.0567 | 13) 9 | 18) 97.58 |
| 4) 209.3 | 9) 733.2 | 14) 0.008 | 19) 2.003 |
| 5) 58 | 10) 0.24 | 15) 1.07 | 20) 0.101 |

# b

Write these numbers and multiply each of them by 100

| | | | |
|---|---|---|---|
| 1) 1.438 | 6) 54.81 | 11) 0.6473 | 16) 4.8181 |
| 2) 29.52 | 7) 663.5 | 12) 58.2 | 17) 62.9 |
| 3) 0.327 | 8) 49.380 | 13) 708.05 | 18) 91.78 |
| 4) 74 | 9) 6.5055 | 14) 2.039 | 19) 0.0013 |
| 5) 16.585 | 10) 8 | 15) 0.0328 | 20) 5.55555 |

# c

Write these numbers and multiply each of them by 1000

| | | | |
|---|---|---|---|
| 1) 6.5382 | 6) 89.87 | 11) 5.3900 | 16) 0.0084 |
| 2) 0.00253 | 7) 34.5678 | 12) 7.83 | 17) 62.052 |
| 3) 14.725 | 8) 0.921 | 13) 638 | 18) 3.9 |
| 4) 9.3008 | 9) 2 | 14) 2.4193 | 19) 68.75 |
| 5) 16 | 10) 68.44 | 15) 16.1 | 20) 0.012 |

# d

Try these

| | | |
|---|---|---|
| 1) 5.13 × 10 | 8) 88.57 × 10 | 15) 69.57 × 10 |
| 2) 0.627 × 100 | 9) 2.148 × 1000 | 16) 28.34 × 1000 |
| 3) 33.485 × 10 | 10) 53 × 100 | 17) 413.705 × 100 |
| 4) 1.5945 × 1000 | 11) 145.7 × 1000 | 18) 74 × 1000 |
| 5) 8 × 10 | 12) 12.5 × 100 | 19) 0.0032 × 10 |
| 6) 6.352 × 100 | 13) 0.79 × 10 | 20) 99.8 × 100 |
| 7) 0.00004 × 1000 | 14) 2.48 × 100 | |

# A ✗ MULTIPLICATION e.g. 62.9 × 0.7

*1) Write out the question,
underlining decimal places
(figures after the point)

62.<u>9</u> × 0.<u>7</u>

*2) Set out as a multiplication
but WITHOUT THE POINTS.
Miss out any LEFT-HAND
noughts.

$$\begin{array}{r} 629 \\ \times \quad 7 \\ \hline \end{array}$$

*3) Work out

$$\begin{array}{r} 629 \\ \times \quad 7 \\ \hline 4403 \end{array}$$

*4) Look back at the question
and count the decimal places.
Your answer should have the
SAME NUMBER OF DECIMAL
PLACES as the question.

62.<u>9</u> × 0.<u>7</u>
= 44.<u>03</u>

---

# B

Long multiplication works out
just the same way

e.g. 2.<u>78</u> × 4.<u>2</u>

$$\begin{array}{r} 278 \\ \times \quad 42 \\ \hline 556 \\ 1112 \\ \hline 11676 \end{array}$$

So 2.<u>78</u> × 4.<u>2</u> = 11.<u>676</u>

---

# C

Fill up to the point with noughts
if necessary

e.g. 0.<u>16</u> × 0.<u>3</u>

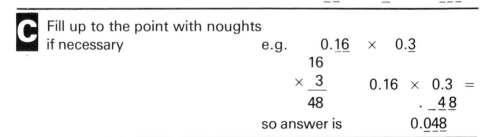

$$\begin{array}{r} 16 \\ \times \quad 3 \\ \hline 48 \end{array}$$

0.16 × 0.3 =
. _<u>48</u>

so answer is

0.<u>048</u>

---

# D

It is better to write 0.942 than .942
The nought helps to show where the point is.

**a** Decimal places have been underlined to help you

1) $6.\underline{2} \times 3$
2) $3.\underline{8} \times 0.\underline{2}$
3) $9.\underline{2} \times 4$
4) $5.\underline{7} \times 0.\underline{5}$
5) $2.\underline{35} \times 6$

6) $3.\underline{44} \times 0.\underline{7}$
7) $2.\underline{06} \times 0.8$
8) $1.\underline{25} \times 2$
9) $39.\underline{2} \times 0.3$
10) $4.\underline{7} \times 0.\underline{05}$

11) $5.\underline{19} \times 0.\underline{4}$
12) $2.\underline{3} \times 11$
13) $92.\underline{3} \times 0.\underline{07}$
14) $4.\underline{8} \times 2.1$
15) $16.\underline{75} \times 0.\underline{6}$

**b** Remember to fill up to the point with noughts if necessary

1) $2.43 \times 0.9$
2) $1.42 \times 0.03$
3) $2.7 \times 3.4$
4) $7.45 \times 0.27$
5) $0.62 \times 5.5$

6) $1.236 \times 0.04$
7) $0.08 \times 0.5$
8) $3.91 \times 24$
9) $62.05 \times 3.6$
10) $2.51 \times 67$

11) $0.175 \times 0.06$
12) $54.4 \times 1.8$
13) $0.38 \times 0.14$
14) $0.085 \times 0.062$
15) $93.7 \times 0.81$

**c**

1) $5.72 \times 0.8$
2) $6.47 \times 2.3$
3) $2.07 \times 1.06$
4) $9.9 \times 9.9$
5) $0.28 \times 0.3$

6) $0.68 \times 29$
7) $1.052 \times 9.6$
8) $67.5 \times 0.08$
9) $0.329 \times 0.2$
10) $0.008 \times 0.09$

11) $7.77 \times 0.55$
12) $0.042 \times 63$
13) $613 \times 400$
14) $2.08 \times 1.35$
15) $343.4 \times 0.061$

**d**

1) Multiply 24.8 by 6
2) Multiply 6.9 by 3.2
3) Multiply 2.075 by 8
4) Multiply 5.15 by 0.05
5) Multiply 94 by 0.1

6) Multiply 7.56 by 0.21
7) Multiply 2.22 by 7.3
8) Multiply 0.59 by 82
9) Multiply 0.27 by 0.004
10) Multiply 4.06 by 3.002

11) Find the product of 1.023 and 0.97
12) Find the product of 1.55 and 7.4
13) Find the product of 0.69 and 0.36
14) Find the product of 7.5 and 0.0003
15) Find the product of 0.28 and 0.28

#  ÷ DIVISION BY 10, 100, 1000, ETC.

NOTICE that the POINT DOES NOT MOVE and the FIGURES STAY THE SAME (except for an extra nought now and then)

---

 **DIVIDE BY 10**
*Move the number
  ONE PLACE SMALLER

e.g.    43.6  ÷  10

          4.36

e.g.    2.87  ÷  10
          0.287

---

 **DIVIDE BY 100**
*Move the number
  TWO PLACES SMALLER

e.g.    359.6  ÷  100

          3.596

e.g.    1.49  ÷  100
          0.0149

**REMEMBER** — Fill up to the point with noughts.

---

 **DIVIDE BY 1000**
*Move the number
  THREE PLACES SMALLER

e.g.   10257      ÷  1000

          10.257

e.g.    35.49  ÷  1000
          0.03549

**REMEMBER** — Fill up to the point with noughts

---

**E**

(1)    It is better to write 0.537 than .537
       The nought helps to show where the point is

(2)    How would you divide by 10000 or 100000?

**a**  Write these numbers and then divide each of them by 10

| | | | |
|---|---|---|---|
| 1) 12.3 | 6) 9.85 | 11) 7538.5 | 16) 600.85 |
| 2) 25.69 | 7) 572.7 | 12) 0.037 | 17) 0.9 |
| 3) 438.1 | 8) 0.328 | 13) 50.03 | 18) 36.012 |
| 4) 73.892 | 9) 11.8904 | 14) 926 | 19) 0.0006 |
| 5) 2134.6 | 10) 8 | 15) 0.051 | 20) 74 |

**b**  Write these numbers and divide each of them by 100

| | | | |
|---|---|---|---|
| 1) 327.8 | 6) 537.9 | 11) 200.5 | 16) 40358 |
| 2) 119.02 | 7) 2.83 | 12) 81 | 17) 329.747 |
| 3) 6845.5 | 8) 14.625 | 13) 999 | 18) 4 |
| 4) 23.48 | 9) 0.5 | 14) 1607.8 | 19) 21.3 |
| 5) 700 | 10) 7342 | 15) 56.65 | 20) 0.08 |

**c**  Write these numbers and divide each of them by 1000

| | | | |
|---|---|---|---|
| 1) 5167.5 | 6) 159.20 | 11) 72000 | 16) 144.85 |
| 2) 23480.6 | 7) 67.84 | 12) 295.75 | 17) 0.78 |
| 3) 5000 | 8) 1243.7 | 13) 31 | 18) 203023 |
| 4) 917.8 | 9) 3008 | 14) 1469.02 | 19) 16.2 |
| 5) 3838.11 | 10) 972 | 15) 78.3 | 20) 9 |

**d**  Try these

| | | |
|---|---|---|
| 1) 892.3 ÷ 100 | 8) 0.65 ÷ 10 | 15) 66 ÷ 10 |
| 2) 417.5 ÷ 10 | 9) 5331 ÷ 100 | 16) 2.75 ÷ 100 |
| 3) 6 ÷ 10 | 10) 88888 ÷ 1000 | 17) 4 ÷ 1000 |
| 4) 3917.25 ÷ 1000 | 11) 95.62 ÷ 100 | 18) 537.2 ÷ 10 |
| 5) 488 ÷ 100 | 12) 3.44 ÷ 10 | 19) 495112 ÷ 1000 |
| 6) 36.4 ÷ 10 | 13) 0.8 ÷ 100 | 20) 0.06 ÷ 100 |
| 7) 773.8 ÷ 1000 | 14) 197 ÷ 1000 | |

#  A ÷ DIVISION by a whole number

e.g.  7.14 ÷ 3

*Keep the point in the ANSWER
above the point in the question

```
         .
3)  7.14
```

```
    2.38
3)  7.14
```

# B RUNNING OUT OF NUMBERS

e.g.  (1)  24.3 ÷ 5

*1) Do NOT put remainders at the
end of a decimal division

```
     4.8 ???
5)  24.3
```

*2) ADD MORE NOUGHTS (as
many as you need) and keep
going

```
     4.86
5)  24.30
```

e.g  (2)  2.9 ÷ 8

```
     0.3 ???
8)  2.9
```

```
     0.3625
8)  2.9000
```

#  C RECURRING DECIMALS (Decimals which go on the same way for ever).

e.g.  (1)  0.47 ÷ 3

```
     0.1566666666   etc.
3)  0.4700000000
```

The 6 goes on for ever, so write  $0.15\dot{6}$

e.g.  (2)  6.43 ÷ 11

```
     0.58454545454
11)  6.43000000000
```

The 45 goes on for ever, so write  $0.58\dot{4}\dot{5}$

**a**

| | | |
|---|---|---|
| *1)* 5.22 ÷ 3 | *6)* 58.3 ÷ 11 | *11)* 6.72 ÷ 24 |
| *2)* 742.5 ÷ 5 | *7)* 11.12 ÷ 4 | *12)* 446.5 ÷ 19 |
| *3)* 0.516 ÷ 2 | *8)* 0.048 ÷ 6 | *13)* 0.1974 ÷ 21 |
| *4)* 48.3 ÷ 7 | *9)* 3.384 ÷ 9 | *14)* 10.8 ÷ 12 |
| *5)* 3.15 ÷ 3 | *10)* 575.2 ÷ 8 | *15)* 1.2062 ÷ 37 |

**b**

Remember to add NOUGHTS if you run out of numbers

| | | |
|---|---|---|
| *1)* 23.4 ÷ 5 | *6)* 0.98 ÷ 5 | *11)* 19.9 ÷ 16 |
| *2)* 9.81 ÷ 6 | *7)* 33.3 ÷ 2 | *12)* 5.1 ÷ 12 |
| *3)* 0.117 ÷ 2 | *8)* 35.1 ÷ 8 | *13)* 90.4 ÷ 25 |
| *4)* 9.7 ÷ 8 | *9)* 2.97 ÷ 6 | *14)* 0.402 ÷ 24 |
| *5)* 51.0 ÷ 4 | *10)* 72.9 ÷ 4 | *15)* 6.3 ÷ 15 |

**c**

The answers to these will be RECURRING DECIMALS

| | | |
|---|---|---|
| *1)* 22.3 ÷ 3 | *6)* 100.6 ÷ 6 | *11)* 44 ÷ 3 |
| *2)* 14.6 ÷ 6 | *7)* 5.79 ÷ 11 | *12)* 0.94 ÷ 11 |
| *3)* 6.84 ÷ 11 | *8)* 0.885 ÷ 9 | *13)* 100.0 ÷ 18 |
| *4)* 2.2 ÷ 9 | *9)* 2.0 ÷ 3 | *14)* 36.7 ÷ 33 |
| *5)* 5.6 ÷ 3 | *10)* 31.6 ÷ 9 | *15)* 23.2 ÷ 7 |

**d**

Try these (different sorts jumbled up)

| | | |
|---|---|---|
| *1)* 82.5 ÷ 3 | *6)* 54.3 ÷ 8 | *11)* 49.5 ÷ 11 |
| *2)* 9.87 ÷ 2 | *7)* 7.6 ÷ 6 | *12)* 35.0 ÷ 12 |
| *3)* 5.2 ÷ 11 | *8)* 3.36 ÷ 7 | *13)* 36.6 ÷ 15 |
| *4)* 0.0124 ÷ 8 | *9)* 0.69 ÷ 6 | *14)* 105 ÷ 27 |
| *5)* 3.002 ÷ 5 | *10)* 6.1 ÷ 9 | *15)* 0.343 ÷ 14 |

#  ÷ DIVISION by a decimal

*1) Write the question     e.g.    1.235 ÷ 0.05

*2) Make the RIGHT-HAND number
into a whole number               ÷ 5
(In this case you have to
multiply it by 100)

*3) Move the LEFT-HAND number
the same amount of places    123.5 ÷ 5
(In this case, multiply it by
100, too)

*4) Set out as usual, keeping the
point in the answer directly
above the point in the question

$$5\overline{)123.5}$$

$$\begin{array}{r} 24.7 \\ 5\overline{)123.5} \end{array}$$

---

## B   Examples of how to start

| | | | | | | |
|---|---|---|---|---|---|---|
| 1) | 3.69 ÷ 0.3 | | 6) | 0.0328 ÷ 0.006 | |
| | 36.9 ÷ 3 | | | 32.8 ÷ 6 | |
| 2) | 43.55 ÷ 1.5 | | 7) | 7.2 ÷ 0.09 | |
| | 435.5 ÷ 15 | | | 720 ÷ 9 | |
| 3) | 9.728 ÷ 0.04 | | 8) | 9.464 ÷ 0.26 | |
| | 972.8 ÷ 4 | | | 946.4 ÷ 26 | |
| 4) | 41.6 ÷ 0.8 | | 9) | 0.5525 ÷ 0.17 | |
| | 416 ÷ 8 | | | 55.25 ÷ 17 | |
| 5) | 258 ÷ 0.43 | | 10) | 62.5 ÷ 0.005 | |
| | 25800 ÷ 43 | | | 62500 ÷ 5 | |

**a**

| | | |
|---|---|---|
| 1) 3.69 ÷ 0.3 | 6) 0.036 ÷ 0.6 | 11) 0.0052 ÷ 0.04 |
| 2) 42.5 ÷ 0.5 | 7) 1.77 ÷ 0.03 | 12) 5.275 ÷ 0.05 |
| 3) 0.632 ÷ 0.4 | 8) 26.8 ÷ 0.4 | 13) 5.275 ÷ 0.005 |
| 4) 5.04 ÷ 0.2 | 9) 1.82 ÷ 1.3 | 14) 0.0006 ÷ 0.002 |
| 5) 7.91 ÷ 0.7 | 10) 5.74 ÷ 1.4 | 15) 0.352 ÷ 0.11 |

**b**

| | | |
|---|---|---|
| 1) 8.74 ÷ 0.1 | 6) 6.24 ÷ 0.5 | 11) 2.301 ÷ 0.3 |
| 2) 52.8 ÷ 0.02 | 7) 0.432 ÷ 1.8 | 12) 0.529 ÷ 2.3 |
| 3) 8.076 ÷ 0.4 | 8) 63.8 ÷ 1.1 | 13) 0.1234 ÷ 0.04 |
| 4) 54.4 ÷ 0.17 | 9) 0.5 ÷ 0.8 | 14) 132 ÷ 0.02 |
| 5) 8.25 ÷ 1.5 | 10) 38.08 ÷ 3.4 | 15) 46.8 ÷ 0.09 |

**c**

| | | |
|---|---|---|
| 1) 3.26 ÷ 0.04 | 6) 96.6 ÷ 0.21 | 11) 0.0657 ÷ 0.9 |
| 2) 59 ÷ 0.5 | 7) 3.272 ÷ 0.8 | 12) 0.0036 ÷ 0.05 |
| 3) 10.2 ÷ 2 | 8) 72.4 ÷ 0.05 | 13) 40.66 ÷ 0.019 |
| 4) 85.8 ÷ 0.12 | 9) 37.6 ÷ 16 | 14) 594 ÷ 2.7 |
| 5) 18.24 ÷ 0.3 | 10) 4.64 ÷ 0.3 | 15) 0.0001 ÷ 0.02 |

**d**

| | |
|---|---|
| 1) Divide 1.56 by 0.4 | 9) Divide 6.252 by 0.03 |
| 2) Divide 28 by 0.5 | 10) Divide 1 by 0.9 |
| 3) Divide 0.408 by 1.2 | 11) Divide 149.1 by 0.07 |
| 4) Divide 28.5 by 30 | 12) Divide 0.896 by 1.28 |
| 5) Divide 38 by 0.8 | 13) Divide 3900 by 0.13 |
| 6) Divide 7.3 by 0.06 | 14) Divide 63.3 by 0.16 |
| 7) Divide 0.06 by 2.5 | 15) Divide 9.594 by 4.1 |
| 8) Divide 13.86 by 3.3 | |

# A ✕ ÷ MULTIPLICATION AND DIVISION

*If there are two or more signs in the same question, DO EACH PART SEPARATELY

e.g.   $4.35 \times 5.2 \div 0.4$

$4.35 \times 5.2 = 22.62$

Then   $22.62 \div 0.4$

$= 56.55$

## Brackets

*If there are brackets, always do the part INSIDE the brackets first

e.g.   $14.4 \div (6.4 \times 0.05)$

$6.4 \times 0.05 = 0.32$

Then   $14.4 \div 0.32$

$= 45$

# B + − ✕ ÷ MIXED DECIMALS

## WITH BRACKETS

*1) Always do the part INSIDE the brackets first

*2) Then do the other parts

e.g.   $4.41 \div (2.34 - 0.54)$

$2.34 - 0.54 = 1.8$

$4.41 \div 1.8$

$= 2.45$

## WITHOUT BRACKETS

*1) Always do ✕ or ÷ first

*2) Then do + or −

e.g.   $3.27 + 3.4 \times 2.6$

$3.4 \times 2.6 = 8.84$

$3.27 + 8.84$

$= 12.11$

# C REMEMBER 'B O M D A S'

| First | **B**rackets |
| **Then** | **O**f, **M**ultiply, **D**ivide |
| Then | **A**dd, **S**ubtract |

**a**

1) 9.4 × 3.6 ÷ 2
2) 66.5 ÷ 0.5 ÷ 0.7
3) 1.7 × 2.5 × 4.2
4) 0.207 ÷ (1.5 × 0.6)
5) 245 × 0.01 ÷ 0.25

6) 325 × 0.2 × 3.6
7) 0.054 × (3.84 ÷ 0.6)
8) 0.8 × 0.2 ÷ 0.005
9) 4.9 ÷ 0.4 × 0.7
10) 0.465 ÷ (38.75 × 0.8)

---

**b**

1) 15.3 + 4.28
2) 9.6 × 0.7
3) 46.1 − 12.8
4) 5.5 ÷ 8
5) 0.693 × 100

6) 0.523 − 0.085
7) 7.38 + 65.904
8) 4.068 ÷ 0.3
9) 6.1 − 1.66
10) 0.44 × 0.123

11) 335.8 ÷ 0.23
12) 13 × 0.064
13) 90 − 5.16
14) 82.82 + 8.282
15) 0.624 ÷ 0.048

---

**c**

1) (0.62 + 1.6) ÷ 0.3
2) 0.16 × (9.3 − 1.55)
3) 4.07 + 15.8 + 0.36
4) (0.0384 + 0.0615) × 1000
5) 0.98 × 1.5 + 3.53
6) 2.5 × 2.5 × 0.6
7) (0.11 − 0.0034) ÷ 1.3
8) 132.3 + 44.4 − 167.6

9) 2.115 ÷ 0.15 + 5.9
10) 0.7474 − (20.2 × 0.037)
11) (2.9 + 0.56) × 1.5
12) 0.59 × (9.3 − 8.71)
13) 35.30 − 7.38 − 26.93
14) 22.14 ÷ (3.6 × 0.05)
15) (5.05 − 4.95) × (4.7 + 5.3)

---

**d**

1) Subtract 0.76 from the sum of 8.69 and 2.73
2) Add 0.021 to the product of 0.14 and 0.7
3) Divide by 22 the sum of 0.55 and 0.99
4) Find the difference between (29 × 0.28) and (3.73 ÷ 0.5)
5) Multiply by 0.5 the difference between 133.3 and 27.2
6) Subtract 0.7 from the product of 64 and 0.025
7) Divide by 0.13 the difference between 0.53 and 0.14
8) Find the sum of 4.74, 474, 0.474 and 47.4
9) Multiply the product of 0.11 and 1.1 by 11
10) Add 8 to the difference between 4.50 and 2.51

# **A** £ p MONEY

Money is worked out the same way as other decimals, but remember . . .

**WHOLE POUNDS** can be written with or without the decimal point

e.g. 'seventy-three pounds' can be written either £73 or £73.00

---

**THE £ SIGN** always comes BEFORE the amount

e.g. £639.00 (never 639.00£)

---

**DECIMAL PLACES** Money is written with TWO decimal places (never more and never less)

e.g. 'four pounds eighty' is written
$$£4.80 \qquad (never £4.8)$$
'sixteen pounds and fivepence' is written
$$£16.05 \qquad (never £16.5)$$

---

**SMALL AMOUNTS,** usually under £1, can be written in PENCE (p)

e.g. £0.67 can be written 67p
£0.08 can be written 8p
£0.93 can be written 93p

---

# **B** CHANGING PENCE INTO POUNDS

e.g. Write in £ this amount 34p

*Divide by 100
$$34 \div 100$$
$$= \quad £0.34$$

e.g. Write 9p in £
$$9 \div 100$$
$$= \quad £0.09$$

To change **pounds** into **pence**, MULTIPLY by 100.

# a

Write these amounts in £

1) 82p  3) 7p  5) 125p  7) 6p  9) 10p
2) 23p  4) 99p  6) 2p  8) 50p  10) 1p

# b

1) £3.27 + £4.88
2) £14.25 ÷ 3
3) £1.42 × 5
4) £8.27 − £3.74
5) £2.05 × 19
6) £16.38 + £23.91
7) £28.32 ÷ 12
8) £66.66 + £58.90
9) £6.50 − £1.74
10) 83p × 22
11) £94.50 ÷ 10
12) £43 + £25.75 + £4.55
13) £9.90 × 50
14) £2.24 + £1.88 − £3.25
15) £142 ÷ 8

# c

Calculate the change you should receive from a £5 note if you spend

1) £3.69  4) £2.58  7) £3.01  9) £4.44
2) £1.27  5) £4.61  8) £0.97  10) £2.72
3) £4.83  6) £1.99

# d

1) Find the cost of 6 railway tickets at £2.34 each
2) Add £14.72, £38.57, £5.84, £21.05
3) A man had £435.68. Then he spent £178.90. How much money did he have left?
4) Ann, Claire and Victoria shared equally £8.55. How much did each receive?
5) Find the cost of 2 cakes at 43p each, 4 bottles of lemonade at 24p each and 6 packets of crisps at 17p each.
6) How much is each person's share if £72.49 is shared equally between 11 people?
7) Mark bought 5 model cars at £1.87 each at a shop. What change should he have received if he gave the shopkeeper 2 £5 notes?
8) 8 people shared equally a £500 prize. How much did each person receive?
9) James earns £28.74 less each week than Fred. If Fred earns £142.12, how much does James earn?
10) Admission to the funfair was £1.25 for an adult and 75p for a child. Mr and Mrs Brown and their 3 children went to the funfair. How much did it cost them altogether?

# A FRACTIONS

A fraction is a PART of a whole thing

e.g.    This pie is shared equally
         between 5 people
         Each person gets $\frac{1}{5}$ of a pie
         (1 pie divided by 5)

$\frac{1}{5}$  is a FRACTION

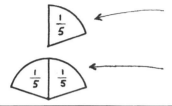

This FRACTION is  $\frac{1}{5}$
(one fifth) of the pie

This FRACTION is  $\frac{2}{5}$
(two fifths) of the pie , etc.

---

# B WHAT SORT OF FRACTION?  HOW MANY?

This shape is divided into
     4 equal parts

e.g.

and 3 parts are
     shaded

$\overline{4}$   ← DENOMINATOR
                  tells you what sort
                  of fraction

$\underline{3}$   ← NUMERATOR
   4               tells you how many

$\frac{3}{4}$ of the shape is shaded.

---

# C A FRACTION IS A DIVISION

The line in the middle of a fraction means 'DIVIDED BY'

e.g. (1)  7 divided by 8 can be written as a fraction     $\frac{7}{8}$

e.g. (2)  If 2 bars of chocolate are shared equally between
          3 people, each person gets $\frac{2}{3}$ of a bar of chocolate
          (2 DIVIDED BY 3)

2 bars of chocolate

divided by 3

$\frac{2}{3}$          $\frac{2}{3}$          $\frac{2}{3}$

# a

In each drawing, what fraction is shaded?

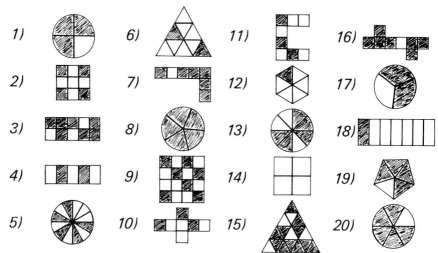

1)
6)
11)
16)

2)
7)
12)
17)

3)
8)
13)
18)

4)
9)
14)
19)

5)
10)
15)
20)

# b

Write these divisions as fractions

1) 2 divided by 5

2) 5 divided by 8

3) 3 divided by 4

4) 7 divided by 12

5) 1 divided by 3

6) 4 divided by 7

7) 8 divided by 3

8) 13 divided by 20

9) 6 divided by 5

10) 9 divided by 10

# c

1) One cake was shared equally by 4 boys. What fraction of the cake did each boy have?

2) Two equal plots of land were shared equally by 3 gardeners. What fraction of land did each gardener have?

3) An amount of money was divided equally between 6 people. What fraction did each have?

4) If 3 is divided by 5, what is the answer as a fraction?

5) 5 buns were shared equally between 6 girls. What fraction of a bun did each girl receive?

6) A path was 8 miles long. Bill walked 7 miles and then stopped. What fraction of the path had he walked along?

7) 2 tonnes of coal were put into 5 boxes so that the same amount of coal was in each box. What fraction of a tonne was in each box?

8) 1 week is divided equally into 7 days. What fraction of a week is each day?

9) A large window was divided into 10 equal small windows. 3 of the small windows had coloured glass in them. What fraction of the large window had coloured glass?

10) A soccer team has 11 players. In a certain team, 5 of the players were married. What fraction of the team was married?

#  MIXED NUMBERS AND IMPROPER FRACTIONS

A **MIXED NUMBER** is a mixture of a whole number and a fraction

e.g. $3\frac{2}{3}$ , $1\frac{3}{4}$

An **IMPROPER FRACTION** is a fraction with its top larger than its bottom

e.g. $\frac{25}{8}$ , $\frac{7}{2}$

#  CHANGING A MIXED NUMBER TO AN IMPROPER FRACTION

(You need to do this often at the beginning of a fraction problem)

e.g. $2\frac{3}{4}$

*1) Whole number times bottom     $2 \times 4 = 8$

*2) Add the top     $8 + 3 = 11$

*3) Put over the bottom     $\frac{11}{4}$

#  CHANGING A WHOLE NUMBER TO AN IMPROPER FRACTION

*Put it over 1     e.g.     $3 = \frac{3}{1}$

$7 = \frac{7}{1}$

# D CHANGING AN IMPROPER FRACTION TO A MIXED NUMBER

(You need to do this often at the end of a fraction problem)

e.g. $\frac{13}{3}$

*1) Divide top by bottom $13 \div 3 = 4$   rem. 1

*2) Put remainder over bottom     $4\frac{1}{3}$

IF THERE IS NO REMAINDER, JUST WRITE THE WHOLE NUMBER

e.g. $\frac{9}{1} = 9$,    $\frac{4}{1} = 4$

**a**  Change these to IMPROPER FRACTIONS

| | | | |
|---|---|---|---|
| 1) $3\frac{1}{3}$ | 6) $4\frac{1}{2}$ | 11) $2\frac{3}{8}$ | 16) $3\frac{5}{6}$ |
| 2) $2\frac{1}{4}$ | 7) $8$ | 12) $6\frac{2}{3}$ | 17) $7\frac{1}{7}$ |
| 3) $4\frac{2}{5}$ | 8) $3\frac{4}{7}$ | 13) $2$ | 18) $2\frac{11}{12}$ |
| 4) $1\frac{3}{7}$ | 9) $5\frac{9}{10}$ | 14) $1\frac{1}{16}$ | 19) $5$ |
| 5) $2\frac{5}{6}$ | 10) $1\frac{1}{2}$ | 15) $4\frac{1}{4}$ | 20) $1\frac{7}{8}$ |

**b**  Write the following as improper fractions

| | | | |
|---|---|---|---|
| 1) $1\frac{7}{12}$ | 6) $4\frac{3}{8}$ | 11) $3\frac{3}{4}$ | 16) $2\frac{3}{5}$ |
| 2) $3\frac{1}{6}$ | 7) $10\frac{1}{3}$ | 12) $2\frac{8}{9}$ | 17) $1\frac{5}{11}$ |
| 3) $6\frac{2}{5}$ | 8) $1\frac{6}{7}$ | 13) $4\frac{7}{10}$ | 18) $7$ |
| 4) $5\frac{1}{2}$ | 9) $1\frac{15}{16}$ | 14) $12$ | 19) $25\frac{1}{2}$ |
| 5) $3$ | 10) $4\frac{1}{8}$ | 15) $5\frac{2}{3}$ | 20) $8\frac{1}{4}$ |

**c**  Change these to MIXED NUMBERS (or whole numbers if there are no remainders)

| | | | |
|---|---|---|---|
| 1) $\frac{3}{2}$ | 6) $\frac{23}{7}$ | 11) $\frac{17}{4}$ | 16) $\frac{21}{8}$ |
| 2) $\frac{4}{3}$ | 7) $\frac{6}{1}$ | 12) $\frac{43}{8}$ | 17) $\frac{37}{10}$ |
| 3) $\frac{7}{4}$ | 8) $\frac{7}{2}$ | 13) $\frac{2}{1}$ | 18) $\frac{54}{5}$ |
| 4) $\frac{10}{7}$ | 9) $\frac{29}{6}$ | 14) $\frac{20}{3}$ | 19) $\frac{13}{6}$ |
| 5) $\frac{12}{5}$ | 10) $\frac{8}{5}$ | 15) $\frac{11}{6}$ | 20) $\frac{11}{2}$ |

**d**  Express the following as mixed numbers (or whole numbers)

| | | | |
|---|---|---|---|
| 1) $\frac{11}{3}$ | 6) $\frac{8}{1}$ | 11) $\frac{11}{4}$ | 16) $\frac{19}{5}$ |
| 2) $\frac{33}{7}$ | 7) $\frac{26}{3}$ | 12) $\frac{17}{11}$ | 17) $\frac{7}{3}$ |
| 3) $\frac{25}{4}$ | 8) $\frac{15}{8}$ | 13) $\frac{24}{1}$ | 18) $\frac{16}{9}$ |
| 4) $\frac{9}{2}$ | 9) $\frac{13}{10}$ | 14) $\frac{9}{5}$ | 19) $\frac{17}{16}$ |
| 5) $\frac{6}{5}$ | 10) $\frac{100}{3}$ | 15) $\frac{47}{2}$ | 20) $\frac{23}{6}$ |

#  CANCELLING to make a fraction simpler.

*Divide top AND bottom by the SAME NUMBER

e.g. (1) Cancel $\dfrac{18}{22}$

2 will divide into top and bottom

$$\dfrac{18 \div 2}{22 \div 2} = \dfrac{9}{11}$$

e.g. (2) Cancel $\dfrac{15}{35}$

5 will divide into top and bottom

$$\dfrac{15 \div 5}{35 \div 5} = \dfrac{3}{7}$$

# B LOWEST TERMS

A fraction in its simplest form is called 'IN ITS LOWEST TERMS'

*To express a fraction in its LOWEST TERMS,
cancel it until you are sure it will not cancel any more

ALWAYS CHOOSE THE LARGEST NUMBER YOU CAN THINK
OF WHICH WILL DIVIDE INTO TOP AND BOTTOM

e.g. $\dfrac{18}{60}$

2 will divide into top and bottom
and 3 will divide into top and bottom
and 6 will divide into top and bottom
so DIVIDE TOP AND BOTTOM BY 6

$$\dfrac{\cancel{18}^{\,3}}{\cancel{60}_{\,10}} = \dfrac{3}{10}$$

**a**  Divide top and bottom of each fraction by 2.

1) $\frac{6}{14}$    3) $\frac{12}{18}$    5) $\frac{22}{24}$    7) $\frac{2}{18}$    9) $\frac{20}{42}$

2) $\frac{2}{8}$    4) $\frac{16}{26}$    6) $\frac{4}{10}$    8) $\frac{8}{34}$    10) $\frac{4}{50}$

---

**b**  Divide top and bottom of each fraction by 3

1) $\frac{9}{12}$    3) $\frac{24}{30}$    5) $\frac{3}{15}$    7) $\frac{33}{36}$    9) $\frac{12}{15}$

2) $\frac{18}{21}$    4) $\frac{6}{9}$    6) $\frac{6}{27}$    8) $\frac{21}{30}$    10) $\frac{3}{18}$

---

**c**  Cancel by 10 (Divide top and bottom of each fraction by 10)

1) $\frac{50}{90}$    3) $\frac{150}{160}$    5) $\frac{90}{100}$    7) $\frac{60}{110}$    9) $\frac{70}{1000}$

2) $\frac{40}{70}$    4) $\frac{100}{130}$    6) $\frac{10}{120}$    8) $\frac{20}{50}$    10) $\frac{30}{80}$

---

**d**  Cancel by 6

1) $\frac{6}{12}$    3) $\frac{24}{30}$    5) $\frac{18}{42}$    7) $\frac{6}{60}$    9) $\frac{66}{84}$

2) $\frac{42}{48}$    4) $\frac{12}{54}$    6) $\frac{36}{66}$    8) $\frac{30}{72}$    10) $\frac{18}{24}$

---

**e**  For each fraction, find a number which will divide into top AND bottom. Use the number you have found to express the fraction in its lowest terms.

1) $\frac{6}{15}$      6) $\frac{3}{12}$      11) $\frac{16}{40}$      16) $\frac{27}{36}$

2) $\frac{10}{25}$      7) $\frac{8}{12}$      12) $\frac{15}{55}$      17) $\frac{50}{100}$

3) $\frac{2}{12}$      8) $\frac{18}{20}$      13) $\frac{21}{27}$      18) $\frac{54}{90}$

4) $\frac{50}{80}$      9) $\frac{4}{20}$      14) $\frac{88}{99}$      19) $\frac{6}{36}$

5) $\frac{12}{18}$      10) $\frac{21}{28}$      15) $\frac{4}{6}$      20) $\frac{36}{60}$

Have you cancelled all these as far as they will go?
Are they all in their lowest terms?

# A CANCELLING WITH A ✕ SIGN

*Divide ONE TOP and ONE BOTTOM by the same number

e.g. (1)

$$\frac{6}{11} \times \frac{5}{9}$$

Both 6 and 9 will divide by 3

$$\frac{^2\cancel{6}}{11} \times \frac{5}{\cancel{9}_3}$$

$$\frac{2}{11} \times \frac{5}{3}$$

---

e.g. (2)

$$\frac{4}{15} \times \frac{5}{7} \times \frac{11}{16}$$

Both 4 and 16 will divide by 4

$$\frac{^1\cancel{4}}{15} \times \frac{5}{7} \times \frac{11}{\cancel{16}_4}$$

$$\frac{1}{15} \times \frac{5}{7} \times \frac{11}{4}$$

Both 15 and 5 will divide by 5

$$_3\frac{1}{\cancel{15}} \times \frac{\cancel{5}^1}{7} \times \frac{11}{4}$$

$$\frac{1}{3} \times \frac{1}{7} \times \frac{11}{4}$$

# a

Cancel these groups of fractions

1) $\frac{1}{3} \times \frac{3}{4}$    6) $\frac{5}{6} \times \frac{1}{15}$    11) $\frac{6}{5} \times \frac{7}{10}$

2) $\frac{2}{3} \times \frac{1}{2}$    7) $\frac{7}{12} \times \frac{6}{5}$    12) $\frac{3}{5} \times \frac{7}{12}$

3) $\frac{3}{7} \times \frac{2}{3}$    8) $\frac{3}{4} \times \frac{16}{25}$    13) $\frac{7}{8} \times \frac{8}{9}$

4) $\frac{2}{3} \times \frac{1}{4}$    9) $\frac{6}{13} \times \frac{1}{9}$    14) $\frac{7}{10} \times \frac{20}{23}$

5) $\frac{5}{6} \times \frac{3}{4}$    10) $\frac{10}{7} \times \frac{2}{5}$    15) $\frac{24}{25} \times \frac{1}{4}$

# b

Cancel these groups of fractions

1) $\frac{2}{3} \times \frac{3}{4}$    6) $\frac{11}{15} \times \frac{7}{11}$    11) $\frac{6}{35} \times \frac{7}{12}$

2) $\frac{1}{5} \times \frac{15}{16}$    7) $\frac{3}{10} \times \frac{5}{21}$    12) $\frac{10}{11} \times \frac{5}{4}$

3) $\frac{5}{3} \times \frac{3}{5}$    8) $\frac{16}{7} \times \frac{7}{8}$    13) $\frac{12}{25} \times \frac{5}{16}$

4) $\frac{7}{8} \times \frac{5}{14}$    9) $\frac{2}{5} \times \frac{25}{4}$    14) $\frac{20}{21} \times \frac{7}{8}$

5) $\frac{4}{5} \times \frac{15}{16}$    10) $\frac{7}{18} \times \frac{2}{3}$    15) $\frac{13}{6} \times \frac{15}{26}$

# c

Cancel these groups of fractions

1) $\frac{1}{4} \times \frac{4}{3} \times \frac{1}{5}$    6) $\frac{1}{3} \times \frac{2}{5} \times \frac{5}{8}$    11) $\frac{25}{4} \times \frac{16}{1} \times \frac{11}{15}$

2) $\frac{7}{8} \times \frac{3}{5} \times \frac{10}{11}$    7) $\frac{3}{8} \times \frac{10}{7} \times \frac{14}{9}$    12) $\frac{8}{39} \times \frac{13}{24}$

3) $\frac{12}{15} \times \frac{11}{18}$    8) $\frac{11}{12} \times \frac{3}{8} \times \frac{5}{22}$    13) $\frac{5}{2} \times \frac{4}{7} \times \frac{7}{2}$

4) $\frac{5}{6} \times \frac{1}{7} \times \frac{12}{13}$    9) $\frac{4}{5} \times \frac{1}{9} \times \frac{1}{10}$    14) $\frac{15}{28} \times \frac{7}{16} \times \frac{8}{25}$

5) $\frac{10}{3} \times \frac{1}{4} \times \frac{8}{15}$    10) $\frac{5}{6} \times \frac{7}{13} \times \frac{9}{20}$    15) $\frac{6}{1} \times \frac{1}{5} \times \frac{17}{18}$

# d

Cancel these groups of fractions. Write any whole numbers as fractions, e.g. write 2 as $\frac{2}{1}$, 5 as $\frac{5}{1}$, etc.

1) $\frac{3}{8} \times \frac{4}{5} \times \frac{1}{3}$    6) $\frac{11}{12} \times \frac{3}{7} \times \frac{35}{26} \times \frac{13}{44}$    11) $\frac{15}{16} \times \frac{5}{48}$

2) $2 \times \frac{7}{8}$    7) $5 \times \frac{9}{65}$    12) $\frac{9}{8} \times 7 \times \frac{32}{35}$

3) $\frac{2}{3} \times 3$    8) $\frac{18}{31} \times \frac{31}{48}$    13) $10 \times \frac{9}{14} \times \frac{7}{25}$

4) $\frac{3}{4} \times \frac{10}{11} \times \frac{8}{9}$    9) $\frac{10}{21} \times \frac{14}{25} \times 6$    14) $\frac{6}{11} \times 4 \times \frac{22}{45}$

5) $\frac{11}{17} \times \frac{51}{55}$    10) $\frac{4}{5} \times \frac{5}{6} \times \frac{5}{8}$    15) $\frac{35}{18} \times \frac{9}{10} \times \frac{4}{7}$

# **A** LOWEST COMMON DENOMINATOR (LCD)

(The bottom of a fraction is called the DENOMINATOR)

*To find the lowest common denominator, look for the lowest number that ALL THE DENOMINATORS WILL DIVIDE INTO

e.g.   (1)                         $\frac{1}{4}$ , $\frac{2}{3}$ , $\frac{1}{2}$

        4 will divide into 12
        3 will divide into 12
        2 will divide into 12

They will not divide into anything smaller,
   so 12 is the LCD

$$\frac{}{12} , \frac{}{12} , \frac{}{12}$$

---

e.g.   (2)                         $\frac{5}{8}$ + $\frac{3}{4}$

        8 will divide into 8
        4 will divide into 8
   so 8 is the LCD

$$\frac{}{8} + \frac{}{8}$$

---

### HINTS

(THESE MAY HELP BUT THEY DO NOT ALWAYS GIVE THE CORRECT LCD)

1) Look at the larger (or largest) denominator.
   Is this the LCD?        $\frac{3}{4}$ , $\frac{5}{12}$

   Yes.   12 is the LCD        $\frac{}{12}$ , $\frac{}{12}$

2) If this will not work, try multiplying the denominators.
   Does this give the LCD?        $\frac{2}{3}$ , $\frac{1}{5}$

Yes.   $3 \times 5 = 15$   so 15 is the LCD        $\frac{}{15}$ , $\frac{}{15}$

**a** Find the LOWEST COMMON DENOMINATOR of each group of fractions (Pretend the tops of the fractions are not there)

1) $\frac{2}{3}$ , $\frac{1}{2}$   6) $\frac{1}{2}$ , $\frac{3}{5}$   11) $\frac{5}{1}$ , $\frac{7}{9}$

2) $\frac{1}{2}$ , $\frac{3}{4}$   7) $\frac{5}{6}$ , $\frac{7}{12}$   12) $\frac{3}{10}$ , $\frac{1}{2}$

3) $\frac{3}{5}$ , $\frac{7}{10}$   8) $\frac{3}{4}$ , $\frac{5}{8}$   13) $\frac{3}{2}$ , $\frac{1}{6}$

4) $\frac{1}{4}$ , $\frac{2}{3}$   9) $\frac{3}{5}$ , $\frac{3}{4}$   14) $\frac{7}{4}$ , $\frac{3}{1}$

5) $\frac{4}{5}$ , $\frac{1}{3}$   10) $\frac{8}{3}$ , $\frac{5}{6}$   15) $\frac{11}{6}$ , $\frac{7}{5}$

**b** Find the LCD of each group (Pretend the tops of the fractions are not there)

1) $\frac{5}{2}$ , $\frac{5}{8}$   6) $\frac{22}{7}$ , $\frac{1}{2}$   11) $\frac{3}{1}$ , $\frac{11}{12}$

2) $\frac{9}{10}$ , $\frac{13}{4}$   7) $\frac{10}{3}$ , $\frac{7}{1}$   12) $\frac{2}{5}$ , $\frac{4}{7}$

3) $\frac{5}{8}$ , $\frac{1}{3}$   8) $\frac{1}{6}$ , $\frac{9}{2}$   13) $\frac{5}{6}$ , $\frac{5}{9}$

4) $\frac{1}{8}$ , $\frac{2}{5}$   9) $\frac{6}{5}$ , $\frac{1}{5}$   14) $\frac{2}{3}$ , $\frac{11}{16}$

5) $\frac{17}{6}$ , $\frac{5}{4}$   10) $\frac{21}{4}$ , $\frac{5}{12}$   15) $\frac{8}{9}$ , $\frac{1}{2}$

**c** Find the LCD of each group (Pretend the tops of the fractions are not there)

1) $\frac{1}{2}$ , $\frac{1}{4}$ , $\frac{1}{8}$   6) $\frac{5}{8}$ , $\frac{3}{4}$ , $\frac{2}{3}$   11) $\frac{6}{7}$ , $\frac{4}{5}$

2) $\frac{3}{4}$ , $\frac{2}{3}$ , $\frac{1}{2}$   7) $\frac{4}{3}$ , $\frac{15}{2}$ , $\frac{7}{6}$   12) $\frac{2}{1}$ , $\frac{5}{2}$ , $\frac{9}{4}$

3) $\frac{7}{8}$ , $\frac{5}{2}$ , $\frac{1}{8}$   8) $\frac{17}{10}$ , $\frac{8}{5}$ , $\frac{1}{2}$   13) $\frac{13}{15}$ , $\frac{9}{10}$ , $\frac{23}{6}$

4) $\frac{5}{3}$ , $\frac{6}{7}$   9) $\frac{3}{8}$ , $\frac{19}{6}$   14) $\frac{1}{4}$ , $\frac{1}{5}$ , $\frac{1}{6}$

5) $\frac{23}{3}$ , $\frac{11}{6}$ , $\frac{5}{4}$   10) $\frac{1}{8}$ , $\frac{3}{1}$ , $\frac{7}{4}$   15) $\frac{1}{2}$ , $\frac{1}{6}$ , $\frac{1}{3}$ , $\frac{1}{4}$

**d** Find the LCD of each group of fractions (Pretend the tops of the fractions and the + and − signs are not there)

1) $\frac{5}{6} + \frac{7}{4}$   6) $\frac{8}{5} - \frac{4}{3}$   11) $\frac{5}{2} + \frac{2}{5} + \frac{3}{4}$

2) $\frac{2}{3} + \frac{3}{4}$   7) $\frac{1}{7} + \frac{3}{4}$   12) $\frac{7}{6} + \frac{3}{4} + \frac{9}{8}$

3) $\frac{7}{10} - \frac{4}{25}$   8) $\frac{1}{2} - \frac{3}{10}$   13) $\frac{4}{1} - \frac{6}{5} - \frac{11}{10}$

4) $\frac{5}{6} + \frac{1}{3}$   9) $\frac{19}{10} - \frac{5}{3}$   14) $\frac{8}{5} + \frac{13}{10} - \frac{7}{6}$

5) $\frac{7}{8} - \frac{1}{2}$   10) $\frac{11}{4} + \frac{3}{20}$   15) $\frac{4}{5} - \frac{2}{7} + \frac{3}{2}$

#  ADDITION

e.g. $3\frac{3}{4} + 1\frac{2}{3}$

*1) If there are any WHOLE NUMBERS, add them first and keep till the end

$4 \quad \frac{3}{4} + \frac{2}{3}$

*2) Find LOWEST COMMON DENOMINATOR

$4 \quad \overline{12} + \overline{12}$

*3) Put in new tops (numerators)

$\frac{3}{4}$

$12 \div 4 = 3$
$3 \times 3 = 9$

$\frac{2}{3}$

$12 \div 3 = 4$
$4 \times 2 = 8$

$4 \quad \frac{9}{12} + \frac{8}{12}$

*4) Add tops
DO NOT CHANGE BOTTOMS

$4 \quad \frac{17}{12}$

*5) If the fraction is improper, change to mixed numbers

$4 \quad 1\frac{5}{12}$

*6) Add on any whole numbers

$4 + 1\frac{5}{12} = 5\frac{5}{12}$

---

e.g. (2) $2\frac{3}{5} + \frac{7}{10} + 3\frac{3}{4}$

$2 + 3 = 5$

$5 \quad \frac{3}{5} + \frac{7}{10} + \frac{3}{4}$

$5 \quad \frac{12}{20} + \frac{14}{20} + \frac{15}{20}$

$5 \quad \frac{41}{20}$

$5 \quad 2\frac{1}{20}$

$7\frac{1}{20}$

e.g. (3) $\frac{5}{6} + \frac{1}{3}$

$\frac{5}{6} + \frac{2}{6}$

$\frac{7}{6}$

$1\frac{1}{6}$

---

NEVER ADD BOTTOMS

**a**

1) $\frac{1}{2} + \frac{1}{3}$　　6) $2\frac{1}{6} + \frac{3}{4}$　　11) $2\frac{4}{5} + 1\frac{1}{2}$　　16) $3\frac{1}{2} + 4\frac{3}{4}$

2) $\frac{1}{4} + \frac{1}{2}$　　7) $2\frac{2}{3} + 1\frac{1}{2}$　　12) $1\frac{1}{2} + 1\frac{5}{6}$　　17) $\frac{7}{10} + 1\frac{1}{2}$

3) $\frac{2}{3} + \frac{3}{4}$　　8) $\frac{4}{9} + \frac{1}{3}$　　13) $\frac{3}{4} + 4\frac{1}{8}$　　18) $\frac{3}{4} + \frac{1}{5}$

4) $\frac{1}{2} + \frac{1}{7}$　　9) $1\frac{1}{3} + 1\frac{1}{4}$　　14) $\frac{2}{5} + \frac{3}{10}$　　19) $2\frac{5}{6} + \frac{2}{3}$

5) $\frac{1}{5} + \frac{3}{5}$　　10) $4 + \frac{3}{8}$　　15) $2\frac{3}{8} + 1\frac{5}{8}$　　20) $3\frac{2}{3} + 1\frac{3}{5}$

**b**

1) $1\frac{2}{3} + 2\frac{2}{3}$　　6) $5\frac{2}{5} + 1\frac{3}{4}$　　11) $3\frac{1}{4} + 6\frac{2}{3}$　　16) $\frac{3}{7} + \frac{1}{3}$

2) $3\frac{7}{12} + 1\frac{1}{2}$　　7) $\frac{3}{5} + 2$　　12) $4 + 1\frac{9}{10}$　　17) $1\frac{3}{8} + 2\frac{7}{8}$

3) $2\frac{3}{4} + 4\frac{1}{2}$　　8) $2\frac{2}{3} + 5\frac{1}{2}$　　13) $\frac{5}{9} + \frac{5}{6}$　　18) $3\frac{4}{5} + \frac{1}{3}$

4) $\frac{3}{8} + \frac{2}{3}$　　9) $2\frac{1}{6} + 3\frac{5}{8}$　　14) $\frac{7}{10} + 3\frac{1}{4}$　　19) $5\frac{3}{5} + 2\frac{1}{2}$

5) $1\frac{3}{4} + 4\frac{7}{8}$　　10) $\frac{7}{8} + \frac{5}{16}$　　15) $2\frac{3}{4} + \frac{5}{6}$　　20) $3\frac{3}{8} + 2\frac{2}{5}$

**c**

Find the sum of each of these groups of numbers

1) $3\frac{3}{4}$, $8\frac{5}{8}$　　6) $3\frac{11}{16}$, $2\frac{1}{4}$　　11) $\frac{1}{2}$, $\frac{1}{3}$, $\frac{1}{4}$

2) $7\frac{5}{6}$, $1\frac{1}{2}$　　7) $5\frac{5}{6}$, $\frac{3}{4}$　　12) $\frac{7}{8}$, $\frac{3}{4}$, $\frac{5}{6}$

3) $5\frac{1}{5}$, $2\frac{1}{4}$　　8) $1\frac{3}{4}$, $2\frac{5}{9}$　　13) $1\frac{2}{3}$, $2\frac{1}{6}$, $\frac{1}{2}$

4) $\frac{1}{6}$, $\frac{3}{5}$　　9) $5\frac{7}{13}$, $1\frac{8}{13}$　　14) $3\frac{1}{2}$, $1\frac{1}{4}$, $2\frac{5}{8}$

5) $\frac{9}{10}$, $3\frac{2}{5}$　　10) $12\frac{2}{3}$, $2\frac{4}{5}$　　15) $\frac{3}{5}$, $1\frac{7}{10}$, $\frac{1}{4}$

**d**

1) $\frac{6}{7} + \frac{3}{7} + \frac{2}{7}$　　9) Find the sum of $3\frac{7}{12}$ and $2\frac{1}{9}$

2) $2\frac{5}{8} + 5\frac{7}{12}$　　10) Find the sum of $6\frac{1}{8}$, $4\frac{3}{5}$ and $\frac{1}{4}$

3) $\frac{2}{3} + \frac{3}{4} + \frac{4}{5}$　　11) Find the sum of $1\frac{5}{6}$, $2\frac{5}{9}$ and $3\frac{1}{3}$

4) $\frac{5}{6} + 2\frac{11}{16}$　　12) Find the sum of $8\frac{1}{4}$ and $7\frac{3}{5}$

5) $\frac{1}{6} + \frac{1}{3} + \frac{3}{4} + \frac{1}{2}$　　13) Find the sum of $13\frac{2}{5}$, $11\frac{1}{3}$ and $8\frac{3}{10}$

6) $2\frac{1}{4} + 8\frac{1}{6}$　　14) Find the sum of $\frac{1}{4}$, $\frac{1}{6}$, $\frac{1}{12}$ and $\frac{1}{9}$

7) $16\frac{3}{5} + 19\frac{2}{3}$　　15) Find the sum of $2\frac{2}{9}$ and $1\frac{3}{8}$

8) $1\frac{9}{10} + \frac{1}{2} + 6\frac{4}{5}$

# SUBTRACTION

e.g. $4\frac{1}{3} - 1\frac{4}{5}$

*1) If there are any WHOLE NUMBERS, subtract them first and keep till the end.

$3\frac{1}{3} - \frac{4}{5}$

*2) Find LOWEST COMMON DENOMINATOR

*3) Put in new tops (numerators)

$3 \quad \frac{}{15} - \frac{}{15}$

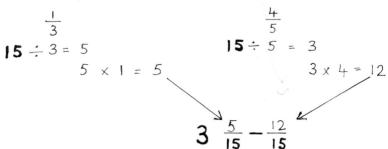

$$\frac{1}{3}$$
$$15 \div 3 = 5$$
$$5 \times 1 = 5$$

$$\frac{4}{5}$$
$$15 \div 5 = 3$$
$$3 \times 4 = 12$$

$$3 \frac{5}{15} - \frac{12}{15}$$

*4) If left top is smaller than right top, borrow a whole one from the whole number

$$3 \qquad \frac{5}{15} - \frac{12}{15}$$

$$2\frac{15}{15} + \frac{5}{15} - \frac{12}{15}$$

*5) Work out tops
DO NOT CHANGE BOTTOMS

$$2\frac{8}{15}$$

---

e.g. (2) $3\frac{1}{5} - 1\frac{3}{4}$

$$2 \quad \frac{1}{5} - \frac{3}{4}$$

$$2 \quad \frac{}{20} - \frac{}{20}$$

$$2 \quad \frac{4}{20} - \frac{15}{20}$$

$$1\frac{20}{20} + \frac{4}{20} - \frac{15}{20}$$

$$1\frac{9}{20}$$

e.g. (3) $5\frac{7}{8} - 1\frac{1}{2}$

$$4 \quad \frac{7}{8} - \frac{1}{2}$$

$$4 \quad \frac{}{8} - \frac{}{8}$$

$$4 \quad \frac{7}{8} - \frac{4}{8}$$

$$4\frac{3}{8}$$

---

NEVER SUBTRACT BOTTOMS

**a**

1) $\frac{4}{5} - \frac{3}{5}$  6) $\frac{3}{4} - \frac{1}{2}$  11) $\frac{7}{12} - \frac{1}{2}$  16) $3\frac{1}{6} - \frac{3}{4}$

2) $\frac{6}{7} - \frac{2}{7}$  7) $\frac{2}{3} - \frac{1}{2}$  12) $\frac{11}{15} - \frac{4}{15}$  17) $3\frac{1}{2} - 1\frac{1}{4}$

3) $\frac{7}{9} - \frac{5}{9}$  8) $\frac{7}{8} - \frac{1}{4}$  13) $1\frac{1}{3} - \frac{1}{2}$  18) $4\frac{1}{10} - 2\frac{1}{2}$

4) $\frac{2}{3} - \frac{1}{3}$  9) $\frac{5}{6} - \frac{2}{3}$  14) $2\frac{1}{4} - \frac{2}{3}$  19) $3\frac{3}{4} - 1\frac{1}{8}$

5) $\frac{9}{11} - \frac{3}{11}$  10) $\frac{9}{10} - \frac{3}{5}$  15) $1\frac{5}{8} - \frac{1}{2}$  20) $2\frac{1}{5} - \frac{1}{4}$

**b**

1) $2\frac{2}{3} - \frac{3}{4}$  6) $3\frac{3}{8} - \frac{3}{4}$  11) $5\frac{1}{9} - 4\frac{2}{3}$  16) $\frac{1}{4} - \frac{1}{9}$

2) $1\frac{1}{6} - \frac{1}{2}$  7) $3\frac{1}{3} - \frac{2}{3}$  12) $2\frac{4}{5} - \frac{1}{10}$  17) $5\frac{1}{2} - 3\frac{2}{3}$

3) $\frac{7}{12} - \frac{3}{8}$  8) $5\frac{1}{5} - \frac{3}{4}$  13) $6\frac{1}{2} - 1\frac{3}{4}$  18) $3\frac{1}{6} - 1\frac{2}{5}$

4) $2\frac{1}{2} - \frac{1}{3}$  9) $3\frac{1}{4} - \frac{5}{6}$  14) $1\frac{3}{4} - \frac{11}{12}$  19) $3\frac{1}{3} - 3\frac{1}{5}$

5) $2\frac{2}{5} - 1\frac{2}{3}$  10) $4\frac{1}{2} - 1\frac{3}{5}$  15) $2\frac{1}{6} - \frac{5}{9}$  20) $2\frac{3}{8} - \frac{5}{6}$

**c**

If necessary, write whole numbers as fractions, e.g. write 4 as $\frac{4}{1}$, 7 as $\frac{7}{1}$, etc.

1) $1\frac{3}{5} - 1\frac{1}{2}$  6) $4\frac{1}{4} - \frac{3}{5}$  11) $\frac{5}{6} - \frac{11}{16}$  16) $4\frac{2}{3} - 1$

2) $2\frac{1}{4} - \frac{9}{10}$  7) $3 - \frac{5}{8}$  12) $2\frac{1}{8} - \frac{5}{8}$  17) $1\frac{5}{16} - \frac{3}{4}$

3) $\frac{1}{2} - \frac{2}{7}$  8) $\frac{11}{15} - \frac{2}{5}$  13) $5 - \frac{5}{6}$  18) $2\frac{1}{10} - \frac{1}{5}$

4) $3\frac{2}{3} - \frac{1}{4}$  9) $8\frac{1}{2} - 2\frac{2}{3}$  14) $1\frac{1}{7} - \frac{4}{5}$  19) $1\frac{5}{6} - \frac{4}{9}$

5) $5\frac{4}{5} - 1\frac{1}{5}$  10) $1\frac{5}{6} - \frac{7}{10}$  15) $2\frac{5}{12} - \frac{5}{8}$  20) $\frac{13}{16} - \frac{7}{12}$

**d**

1) $2\frac{1}{3} - \frac{5}{8}$  11) From $3\frac{1}{4}$ subtract $2\frac{1}{2}$

2) $1\frac{1}{2} - \frac{3}{11}$  12) From $2\frac{1}{3}$ subtract $\frac{8}{9}$

3) $2\frac{1}{6} - 1\frac{3}{4}$  13) From $6\frac{1}{2}$ subtract $1\frac{4}{5}$

4) $6 - 1\frac{1}{4}$  14) From 10 subtract $2\frac{2}{3}$

5) $2\frac{3}{7} - \frac{6}{7}$  15) Find the difference between $4\frac{5}{6}$ and $4\frac{1}{4}$

6) $\frac{11}{20} - \frac{11}{24}$  16) Find the difference between $3\frac{1}{3}$ and $\frac{5}{7}$

7) $2\frac{3}{10} - \frac{1}{4}$  17) Find the difference between $2\frac{1}{8}$ and $\frac{7}{16}$

8) $2\frac{1}{2} - 1\frac{7}{9}$  18) Subtract $\frac{10}{11}$ from $1\frac{1}{3}$

9) $1\frac{1}{9} - \frac{7}{12}$  19) Subtract $\frac{5}{6}$ from $2\frac{1}{9}$

10) $4 - \frac{5}{12}$  20) Subtract $\frac{1}{6}$ from $3\frac{2}{3}$

# A +− ADDITION & SUBTRACTION

Before you do these, make sure you have studied pages
34 and 36.

e.g. $2\frac{1}{4} + \frac{5}{8} - 1\frac{1}{2}$

*1) If there are any WHOLE
NUMBERS, add or subtract
first and keep till the end

$1 \quad \frac{1}{4} + \frac{5}{8} - \frac{1}{2}$

*2) Find LOWEST COMMON
DENOMINATOR

$1 \quad \overline{8} + \overline{8} - \overline{8}$

*3) Put in new tops (numerators)

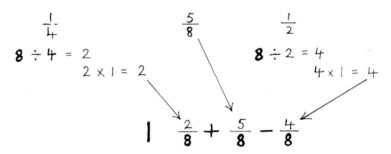

$\frac{1}{4}$    $\frac{5}{8}$    $\frac{1}{2}$

$8 \div 4 = 2$      $8 \div 2 = 4$

$2 \times 1 = 2$      $4 \times 1 = 4$

$1 \quad \frac{2}{8} + \frac{5}{8} - \frac{4}{8}$

*4) Add or subtract tops
   DO NOT CHANGE BOTTOMS

$1 \frac{3}{8}$

---

e.g. (2)

$4\frac{1}{5} - 1\frac{3}{4} + \frac{3}{10}$

$3 \quad \frac{1}{5} - \frac{3}{4} + \frac{3}{10}$

$3 \quad \frac{4}{20} - \frac{15}{20} + \frac{6}{20}$

$2\frac{20}{20} + \frac{4}{20} - \frac{15}{20} + \frac{6}{20}$

$2 \quad \frac{\cancel{15}\ 3}{\cancel{20}\ 4}$

$2\frac{3}{4}$

e.g. (3)

$2\frac{2}{3} + 3\frac{3}{4} - 1\frac{1}{6}$

$4 \quad \frac{2}{3} + \frac{3}{4} - \frac{1}{6}$

$4 \quad \frac{8}{12} + \frac{9}{12} - \frac{2}{12}$

$4 \quad \frac{\cancel{15}\ 5}{\cancel{12}\ 4}$

$4 \quad \frac{5}{4}$

$5\frac{1}{4}$

---

NEVER ADD OR SUBTRACT BOTTOMS

**a**

1) $\frac{7}{8} + \frac{2}{3}$

2) $\frac{1}{3} + 1\frac{3}{5}$

3) $2\frac{3}{4} - \frac{5}{8}$

4) $\frac{8}{9} + 1\frac{1}{3}$

5) $3\frac{1}{2} - 1\frac{5}{6}$

6) $1\frac{1}{6} - \frac{2}{9}$

7) $6\frac{3}{4} + 2\frac{1}{2}$

8) $\frac{5}{8} - \frac{3}{5}$

9) $2\frac{2}{5} - \frac{9}{10}$

10) $\frac{1}{2} + 2\frac{1}{9}$

11) $4\frac{1}{4} - \frac{2}{3}$

12) $3 - 1\frac{1}{7}$

13) $2\frac{7}{12} + 1\frac{5}{9}$

14) $4\frac{1}{2} + 1\frac{2}{5}$

15) $\frac{5}{6} - \frac{11}{15}$

---

**b**

1) $3\frac{1}{6} - \frac{3}{4}$

2) $7\frac{5}{16} + 3\frac{3}{8}$

3) $6 - 3\frac{1}{8}$

4) $2\frac{3}{10} - \frac{1}{3}$

5) $2\frac{15}{16} + 1\frac{1}{12}$

6) Find the sum of $2\frac{3}{7}$ and $7\frac{2}{3}$

7) From $1\frac{1}{5}$ subtract $\frac{2}{3}$

8) Find the difference between $2\frac{1}{4}$ and $1\frac{1}{5}$

9) What is the sum of $3\frac{5}{6}$ and $4\frac{3}{8}$?

10) Subtract $\frac{5}{8}$ from $3\frac{1}{4}$

---

**c**

1) $1\frac{3}{4} + 2\frac{1}{2} + \frac{3}{8}$

2) $\frac{3}{4} + \frac{2}{3} - \frac{5}{6}$

3) $2\frac{1}{2} - \frac{3}{4} - \frac{7}{16}$

4) $3\frac{2}{3} + \frac{1}{6} - 1\frac{3}{4}$

5) $2\frac{7}{10} - 1\frac{1}{4} - \frac{3}{5}$

6) $\frac{8}{9} + 2\frac{1}{3} - 1\frac{5}{6}$

7) $\frac{3}{5} + \frac{5}{6} - \frac{1}{10}$

8) $1\frac{3}{4} + 1\frac{3}{5} - \frac{1}{2}$

9) $2\frac{3}{5} - 1\frac{3}{10} + \frac{1}{2}$

10) $1\frac{5}{9} + \frac{1}{4} - \frac{5}{6}$

---

**d**

1) Find the sum of $1\frac{2}{3}$, $2\frac{3}{4}$ and $3\frac{4}{5}$

2) From the sum of $3\frac{2}{3}$ and $1\frac{1}{2}$ subtract $2\frac{5}{6}$

3) Subtract $4\frac{1}{2}$ from the sum of $2\frac{7}{8}$ and $1\frac{3}{4}$

4) Find the difference between $1\frac{1}{7}$ and $\frac{3}{4}$

5) From the sum of $1\frac{1}{4}$ and $2\frac{2}{3}$ subtract $\frac{7}{12}$

6) Add $3\frac{4}{5}$ to the difference between $2\frac{1}{10}$ and $\frac{1}{2}$

7) Subtract $\frac{5}{8}$ from the sum of $\frac{2}{3}$ and $\frac{1}{6}$

8) Add $2\frac{3}{10}$ to the sum of $3\frac{2}{5}$ and $1\frac{2}{3}$

9) From the sum of $2\frac{1}{2}$ and $1\frac{1}{3}$ subtract $3\frac{4}{9}$

10) Subtract $1\frac{9}{10}$ from the difference between $3\frac{1}{2}$ and $\frac{3}{5}$

#  MULTIPLICATION

e.g. $\frac{2}{5} \times 3\frac{3}{4}$

*1) Turn any mixed numbers to IMPROPER fractions

$\frac{2}{5} \times \frac{15}{4}$

*2) CANCEL if you can

$\frac{1\,\cancel{2}}{\cancel{5}_1} \times \frac{\cancel{15}^3}{\cancel{4}_2}$

*3) Multiply
(TOPS × TOPS, BOTTOMS × BOTTOMS)   $\frac{1}{1} \times \frac{3}{2} = \frac{3}{2}$

*4) If improper, change to mixed numbers

$1\frac{1}{2}$

---

e.g. (2)

$1\frac{5}{9} \times \frac{3}{20} \times 3\frac{4}{7}$

$\frac{14}{9} \times \frac{3}{20} \times \frac{25}{7}$

$\frac{\cancel{14}^2}{\cancel{9}_3} \times \frac{\cancel{3}^1}{\cancel{20}_{4\,2}} \times \frac{\cancel{25}^5}{\cancel{7}_1}$

$\frac{5}{6}$

e.g. (3)

$1\frac{1}{6} \times 2\frac{2}{3}$

$\frac{7}{6} \times \frac{8}{3}$

$\frac{7}{\cancel{6}_3} \times \frac{\cancel{8}^4}{3}$

$\frac{28}{9}$

$3\frac{1}{9}$

---

## B   OF   means 'multiplied by'

e.g. $\frac{7}{16}$ of $4\frac{4}{5}$

$\frac{7}{16} \times 4\frac{4}{5}$

$\frac{7}{16} \times \frac{24}{5}$

$\frac{7}{\cancel{16}_2} \times \frac{\cancel{24}^3}{5}$

$\frac{21}{10}$

$2\frac{1}{10}$

e.g. $\frac{1}{9}$ of $\frac{3}{4}$ of $54$

$\frac{1}{9} \times \frac{3}{4} \times \frac{54}{1}$

$\frac{1}{\cancel{9}_1} \times \frac{3}{\cancel{4}_2} \times \frac{\cancel{54}^{6\ 3}}{1}$

$\frac{9}{2}$

$4\frac{1}{2}$

## a

1) $\frac{1}{4} \times \frac{1}{2}$  6) $1\frac{1}{3} \times \frac{1}{4}$  11) $\frac{5}{7} \times 1\frac{3}{4}$  16) $\frac{7}{8} \times \frac{4}{5}$

2) $\frac{2}{3} \times \frac{1}{5}$  7) $4\frac{2}{5} \times \frac{3}{11}$  12) $1\frac{1}{2} \times \frac{5}{8}$  17) $1\frac{1}{4} \times 3\frac{3}{5}$

3) $\frac{3}{4} \times \frac{5}{8}$  8) $1\frac{3}{7} \times 2\frac{4}{5}$  13) $3\frac{3}{8} \times 1\frac{1}{3}$  18) $2\frac{2}{5} \times 1\frac{1}{9}$

4) $\frac{3}{8} \times \frac{4}{5}$  9) $1\frac{1}{5} \times \frac{7}{12}$  14) $2\frac{1}{2} \times 2\frac{1}{2}$  19) $2\frac{3}{4} \times 1\frac{1}{3}$

5) $\frac{2}{7} \times \frac{1}{6}$  10) $\frac{2}{9} \times \frac{3}{4}$  15) $\frac{9}{10} \times \frac{2}{3}$  20) $\frac{7}{10} \times 2\frac{1}{2}$

## b

Write any whole numbers as fractions,
e.g. Write 8 as $\frac{8}{1}$, 13 as $\frac{13}{1}$, etc.

1) $2\frac{1}{3} \times 2\frac{1}{4}$  6) $\frac{5}{8} \times 7$  11) $\frac{4}{5} \times \frac{5}{6} \times \frac{2}{3}$

2) $1\frac{3}{7} \times 2\frac{5}{8}$  7) $\frac{3}{4}$ of $\frac{1}{6}$  12) $1\frac{1}{3} \times \frac{9}{10} \times 1\frac{1}{4}$

3) $6 \times 1\frac{1}{4}$  8) $\frac{2}{7} \times 8\frac{3}{4}$  13) $\frac{1}{5}$ of $\frac{3}{4}$ of $1000$

4) $2\frac{7}{10} \times 1\frac{5}{9}$  9) $1\frac{1}{11} \times 3\frac{1}{7}$  14) $1\frac{1}{4} \times 8 \times \frac{7}{15}$

5) $2\frac{1}{2} \times \frac{2}{5}$  10) $\frac{7}{8}$ of $12$  15) $\frac{3}{4}$ of $\frac{2}{3}$ of $84$

## c

1) $3\frac{1}{9} \times 5\frac{1}{4}$  6) $\frac{1}{11} \times 6\frac{3}{5}$  11) $\frac{5}{6}$ of $\frac{1}{3}$ of $27$

2) $1\frac{3}{7} \times 1\frac{1}{20}$  7) $\frac{9}{10}$ of $2\frac{2}{3}$  12) $\frac{7}{12} \times 3\frac{1}{5} \times 1\frac{7}{8}$

3) $\frac{2}{5}$ of $\frac{3}{7}$  8) $\frac{5}{6} \times 5\frac{1}{4}$  13) $2\frac{2}{9} \times \frac{3}{11} \times 1\frac{1}{10}$

4) $8 \times \frac{5}{12}$  9) $4\frac{4}{7} \times 1\frac{1}{6}$  14) $\frac{3}{16}$ of $\frac{1}{3}$ of $4\frac{4}{5}$

5) $4\frac{4}{5} \times 3\frac{3}{4}$  10) $\frac{1}{5}$ of $3\frac{1}{3}$  15) $1\frac{1}{2} \times 1\frac{1}{2} \times 1\frac{1}{2}$

## d

1) $1\frac{1}{14} \times 2\frac{1}{10}$  11) Multiply $\frac{3}{8}$ by $1\frac{7}{9}$

2) $7\frac{2}{7} \times 1\frac{4}{17}$  12) Multiply $1\frac{1}{15}$ by $1\frac{1}{8}$

3) $2\frac{1}{5} \times 1\frac{1}{6}$  13) Multiply $2\frac{1}{10}$ by $2\frac{2}{7}$

4) $4\frac{1}{2} \times 2\frac{2}{5}$  14) Multiply $4\frac{1}{5}$ by $1\frac{3}{8}$

5) $6\frac{3}{4} \times 1\frac{1}{9}$  15) Multiply $\frac{1}{6}$ by $7\frac{1}{2}$

6) $\frac{7}{12} \times 7\frac{1}{5}$  16) Find the product of $5\frac{3}{5}$ and $1\frac{4}{21}$

7) $3\frac{7}{16} \times 2\frac{6}{11}$  17) Find the product of $1\frac{4}{5}$ and $\frac{1}{12}$

8) $11\frac{1}{4} \times 3\frac{1}{3}$  18) Find the product of $\frac{22}{25}$ and $1\frac{7}{8}$

9) $\frac{1}{99} \times 7\frac{7}{10}$  19) Find the product of $6$, $1\frac{2}{3}$ and $\frac{7}{10}$

10) $5\frac{2}{5} \times 7\frac{11}{12}$  20) Find the product of $\frac{5}{8}$, $\frac{4}{11}$ and $\frac{11}{15}$

# A ÷ DIVISION

DIVISION is just like multiplication except for an important extra rule (*2)

e.g. $3\frac{3}{5} \div 2\frac{1}{10}$

*1) Turn any mixed numbers to IMPROPER (top-heavy) fractions

$\frac{18}{5} \div \frac{21}{10}$

*2) TURN RIGHT-HAND FRACTION UPSIDE-DOWN

CHANGE ÷ TO ×

$\frac{18}{5} \times \frac{10}{21}$

*3) Cancel if you can

$\frac{\overset{6}{\cancel{18}}}{\underset{1}{\cancel{5}}} \times \frac{\overset{2}{\cancel{10}}}{\underset{7}{\cancel{21}}}$

*4) Multiply (top × top, bottom × bottom)

$\frac{12}{7}$

*5) If improper (top-heavy) change to mixed number

$1\frac{5}{7}$

# B

If you are given a problem like

$\dfrac{1\frac{1}{2}}{1\frac{5}{6}}$ ← this line means DIVIDE

so set it out as a division and go on as usual

$1\frac{1}{2} \div 1\frac{5}{6}$

$\frac{3}{2} \div \frac{11}{6}$

$\frac{3}{2} \times \frac{6}{11}$

$\frac{3}{\underset{1}{\cancel{2}}} \times \frac{\overset{3}{\cancel{6}}}{11}$

$\frac{9}{11}$

**a**

1) $\frac{2}{5} \div \frac{3}{5}$  6) $\frac{5}{6} \div \frac{2}{3}$  11) $\frac{7}{10} \div \frac{3}{5}$  16) $1\frac{1}{2} \div 1\frac{1}{5}$

2) $\frac{1}{8} \div \frac{3}{4}$  7) $\frac{1}{4} \div \frac{5}{8}$  12) $1\frac{1}{2} \div \frac{2}{3}$  17) $1\frac{1}{3} \div 2\frac{1}{2}$

3) $\frac{3}{5} \div \frac{1}{10}$  8) $\frac{2}{3} \div 1\frac{5}{6}$  13) $\frac{3}{4} \div 1\frac{1}{8}$  18) $3\frac{3}{4} \div 1\frac{1}{5}$

4) $\frac{1}{2} \div \frac{7}{8}$  9) $\frac{7}{8} \div \frac{7}{8}$  14) $1\frac{5}{6} \div \frac{1}{3}$  19) $3\frac{1}{4} \div 4\frac{1}{3}$

5) $\frac{3}{8} \div \frac{1}{2}$  10) $2\frac{1}{3} \div \frac{5}{6}$  15) $2\frac{2}{3} \div \frac{2}{3}$  20) $1\frac{1}{4} \div \frac{10}{11}$

---

**b**

1) $4\frac{2}{5} \div 3\frac{3}{10}$  6) $1\frac{3}{4} \div \frac{7}{10}$  11) $2\frac{2}{3} \div \frac{1}{4}$  16) $3\frac{3}{4} \div 1\frac{4}{5}$

2) $1\frac{3}{4} \div 4\frac{1}{5}$  7) $5\frac{2}{3} \div 1\frac{1}{6}$  12) $1\frac{2}{5} \div 1\frac{3}{11}$  17) $4\frac{1}{8} \div 2\frac{3}{4}$

3) $5\frac{4}{5} \div \frac{4}{5}$  8) $3\frac{3}{5} \div 2\frac{1}{10}$  13) $2\frac{3}{5} \div 5\frac{1}{5}$  18) $3\frac{1}{7} \div 5\frac{1}{2}$

4) $\frac{1}{32} \div \frac{5}{8}$  9) $4\frac{2}{3} \div \frac{7}{8}$  14) $1\frac{5}{6} \div 3\frac{1}{7}$  19) $4\frac{1}{2} \div 1\frac{1}{2}$

5) $1\frac{1}{3} \div \frac{2}{9}$  10) $5\frac{1}{4} \div 2\frac{3}{16}$  15) $3\frac{1}{9} \div 1\frac{1}{6}$  20) $3\frac{5}{6} \div 1\frac{1}{2}$

---

**c**

Write any whole numbers as fractions,
e.g. Write 2 as $\frac{2}{1}$ , 5 as $\frac{5}{1}$ , 14 as $\frac{14}{1}$ , etc.

1) $3\frac{1}{5} \div 1\frac{7}{15}$  6) $5\frac{1}{4} \div 7$  11) $1 \div 3\frac{1}{3}$  16) $2\frac{2}{9} \div 1\frac{2}{3}$

2) $2\frac{5}{8} \div 4\frac{2}{3}$  7) $3\frac{3}{4} \div 4\frac{2}{7}$  12) $3\frac{1}{4} \div 4\frac{1}{3}$  17) $6\frac{2}{3} \div \frac{5}{9}$

3) $3 \div 1\frac{1}{4}$  8) $3\frac{1}{5} \div 4$  13) $1\frac{1}{4} \div \frac{5}{6}$  18) $12 \div 3\frac{3}{4}$

4) $1\frac{1}{2} \div 1\frac{1}{5}$  9) $12\frac{1}{4} \div 3\frac{1}{2}$  14) $\frac{1}{12} \div 1\frac{1}{4}$  19) $4\frac{1}{6} \div 10$

5) $3\frac{1}{3} \div 5$  10) $15 \div 3$  15) $4 \div 2\frac{1}{5}$  20) $1\frac{5}{7} \div 1\frac{7}{8}$

---

**d**

1) $\dfrac{\frac{1}{4}}{\frac{3}{4}}$  4) $\dfrac{\frac{5}{6}}{2\frac{1}{12}}$  7) $\dfrac{1\frac{3}{10}}{\frac{4}{5}}$  10) $\dfrac{5\frac{5}{6}}{1\frac{1}{4}}$  13) $\dfrac{2\frac{1}{4}}{1\frac{3}{8}}$

2) $\dfrac{3\frac{1}{3}}{2\frac{1}{2}}$  5) $\dfrac{2\frac{5}{8}}{14}$  8) $\dfrac{\frac{7}{10}}{\frac{2}{5}}$  11) $\dfrac{10}{1\frac{2}{3}}$  14) $\dfrac{\frac{7}{8}}{4\frac{2}{3}}$

3) $\dfrac{\frac{5}{16}}{\frac{1}{4}}$  6) $\dfrac{1\frac{2}{3}}{1\frac{3}{7}}$  9) $\dfrac{5\frac{1}{4}}{1\frac{1}{2}}$  12) $\dfrac{3\frac{3}{4}}{2\frac{2}{3}}$  15) $\dfrac{8}{\frac{1}{4}}$

44

 **A** ✕, ÷ **MULTIPLICATION AND DIVISION**

e.g. $3\frac{1}{4} \times 1\frac{7}{10} \div 5\frac{1}{5}$

*1) Turn any mixed numbers into IMPROPER fractions

$$\frac{13}{4} \times \frac{17}{10} \div \frac{26}{5}$$

*2) INVERT (turn upside-down) any **division** and change ÷ to ✕

$$\frac{13}{4} \times \frac{17}{10} \times \frac{5}{26}$$

*3) Cancel if you can

$$\frac{\overset{1}{\cancel{13}}}{4} \times \frac{17}{\underset{2}{\cancel{10}}} \times \frac{\overset{1}{\cancel{5}}}{\underset{2}{\cancel{26}}}$$

*4) Multiply (top × top, bottom × bottom)

$$\frac{17}{16}$$

*5) If improper (top-heavy) change to a mixed number

$$1\frac{1}{16}$$

---

e.g. (2)

$$2\frac{2}{3} \div \frac{4}{5} \times 1\frac{1}{8}$$

$$\frac{8}{3} \div \frac{4}{5} \times \frac{9}{8}$$

$$\frac{8}{3} \times \frac{5}{4} \times \frac{9}{8}$$

$$\frac{\overset{1}{\cancel{8}}}{\cancel{3}_1} \times \frac{5}{4} \times \frac{\overset{3}{\cancel{9}}}{\cancel{8}_1}$$

$$\frac{15}{4}$$

$$3\frac{3}{4}$$

e.g. (3)

$$3\frac{1}{8} \div 1\frac{1}{4} \div 2\frac{6}{7}$$

$$\frac{25}{8} \div \frac{5}{4} \div \frac{20}{7}$$

$$\frac{25}{8} \times \frac{4}{5} \times \frac{7}{20}$$

$$\frac{\overset{1}{\cancel{5}}\cancel{25}}{\cancel{8}_2} \times \frac{\overset{1}{\cancel{4}}}{\cancel{5}_1} \times \frac{7}{\cancel{20}_4}$$

$$\frac{7}{8}$$

---

**B** If you are given a problem like

$$\frac{1\frac{2}{3} \times \frac{4}{5}}{\frac{1}{3} \times 1\frac{1}{4}}$$ ← this line means DIVIDE

*1) Work out the top

$$1\frac{2}{3} \times \frac{4}{5} = \frac{4}{3}$$

*2) Work out the bottom

$$\frac{1}{3} \times 1\frac{1}{4} = \frac{5}{12}$$

*3) DIVIDE top by bottom

$$\frac{4}{3} \div \frac{5}{12} = 3\frac{1}{5}$$

**a**

1) $\frac{3}{10} \times 3\frac{1}{3}$

2) $6\frac{3}{4} \div \frac{9}{10}$

3) $1\frac{1}{9} \times 3\frac{3}{8}$

4) $4\frac{2}{3} \times 2\frac{1}{7}$

5) $4\frac{1}{6} \div 1\frac{2}{3}$

6) $3\frac{3}{4} \times 1\frac{4}{5}$

7) $2\frac{1}{12} \div 2\frac{1}{3}$

8) $10 \div \frac{5}{12}$

9) $1\frac{4}{7} \times 2\frac{2}{3}$

10) $5\frac{1}{9} \div 3\frac{5}{6}$

11) $5\frac{1}{3} \div 4$

12) $\frac{5}{6} \times 5\frac{1}{5}$

13) $3\frac{3}{5} \times \frac{3}{4}$

14) $1\frac{2}{7} \times 5\frac{5}{6}$

15) $\frac{20}{21} \div 1\frac{1}{14}$

---

**b**

1) $\frac{2}{3} \times \frac{1}{4} \div \frac{5}{9}$

2) $1\frac{3}{5} \times \frac{2}{3} \times 1\frac{1}{4}$

3) $\frac{1}{4} \div \frac{1}{5} \times \frac{1}{3}$

4) $1\frac{1}{3} \div \frac{7}{15} \div 2$

5) $5\frac{1}{2} \times \frac{9}{10} \div 4\frac{2}{5}$

6) $1\frac{1}{6} \div \frac{5}{8} \times 2\frac{1}{7}$

7) $8\frac{3}{4} \div 1\frac{7}{8} \div \frac{5}{6}$

8) $2\frac{2}{3} \times \frac{1}{2} \div 1\frac{3}{5}$

9) $6 \div \frac{2}{3} \div 5$

10) $\frac{9}{10} \times 6\frac{1}{4} \div \frac{3}{7}$

11) Divide by $5\frac{1}{3}$ the product of $\frac{4}{5}$ and $3\frac{1}{3}$

12) Find the product of $2\frac{5}{8}$ and $\left( 3\frac{2}{7} \div 5\frac{3}{4} \right)$

13) Multiply by $1\frac{1}{2}$ the result of dividing $2\frac{2}{3}$ by $4$

14) Divide $8\frac{1}{4}$ by the product of $1\frac{5}{6}$ and $\frac{3}{5}$

15) Multiply the product of $\frac{7}{8}$ and $\frac{5}{8}$ by $\frac{3}{8}$

---

**c**

1) $\dfrac{1\frac{2}{3} \times \frac{7}{10}}{2\frac{4}{5}}$

2) $\dfrac{2\frac{1}{2} \div 1\frac{1}{3}}{2\frac{1}{12}}$

3) $\dfrac{4\frac{1}{5}}{\frac{2}{3} \times \frac{7}{10}}$

4) $\dfrac{3\frac{2}{5} \times 1\frac{2}{3}}{1\frac{1}{3} \times 4\frac{1}{4}}$

5) $\dfrac{3\frac{9}{10} \div 6\frac{1}{2}}{\frac{7}{15}}$

6) $\dfrac{\frac{5}{12} \div \frac{7}{8}}{\frac{5}{8} \times \frac{1}{3}}$

7) $\dfrac{4\frac{2}{3} \times 3\frac{1}{7}}{2\frac{1}{5}}$

8) $\dfrac{6\frac{3}{5}}{6\frac{2}{3} \div \frac{10}{11}}$

9) $\dfrac{8}{\frac{2}{3} \times 3\frac{1}{5}}$

10) $\dfrac{5\frac{1}{4} \times \frac{2}{3}}{\frac{1}{4} \times 1\frac{1}{2}}$

# A $+, -, \times, \div$ MIXED

## WITH BRACKETS

e.g. $\left(2\frac{2}{3} + 3\frac{1}{6}\right) \div 5\frac{1}{4}$

\*1) Always do the parts INSIDE the brackets first

$$\left(\frac{8}{3} + \frac{19}{6}\right) \div 5\frac{1}{4}$$

$$\left(\frac{16}{6} + \frac{19}{6}\right) \div 5\frac{1}{4}$$

$$\frac{35}{6} \div 5\frac{1}{4}$$

\*2) Then do the other parts

$$\frac{35}{6} \div \frac{21}{4}$$

$$\frac{\cancel{35}^{5}}{\cancel{6}_3} \times \frac{\cancel{4}^{2}}{\cancel{21}_3}$$

$$\frac{10}{9}$$

$$1\frac{1}{9}$$

---

## B WITHOUT BRACKETS

e.g. $1\frac{1}{3} - \frac{3}{10} \times 2\frac{1}{2}$

\*1) Always do $\times$ or $\div$ first

$$1\frac{1}{3} - \frac{3}{10} \times \frac{5}{2}$$

$$1\frac{1}{3} - \frac{3}{\cancel{10}_2} \times \frac{\cancel{5}^{1}}{2}$$

$$1\frac{1}{3} - \frac{3}{4}$$

\*2) Then do $+$ or $-$

$$1 \qquad \frac{1}{3} - \frac{3}{4}$$

$$\frac{12}{12} + \frac{4}{12} - \frac{9}{12}$$

$$\frac{7}{12}$$

---

## C

If you are given a problem like

$$\frac{2\frac{3}{4} + 1\frac{1}{3}}{1\frac{1}{3} - \frac{2}{5}} \longleftarrow \text{this line means DIVIDE}$$

\*1) Work out the top $\qquad 2\frac{3}{4} + 1\frac{1}{3} = 4\frac{1}{12}$

\*2) Work out the bottom $\qquad 1\frac{1}{3} - \frac{2}{5} = \frac{14}{15}$

\*3) DIVIDE top by bottom $\qquad 4\frac{1}{12} \div \frac{14}{15} = 4\frac{3}{8}$

---

## D REMEMBER 'B O M D A S'

First     **B**rackets

Then     **O**f, **M**ultiply, **D**ivide

Then     **A**dd, **S**ubtract

**a**

1) $2\frac{1}{4} + 3\frac{2}{3}$    6) $2\frac{2}{4} \div 3\frac{1}{7}$    11) $3\frac{3}{10} - 1\frac{2}{5}$    16) $2\frac{1}{12} \div 3\frac{3}{4}$

2) $1\frac{7}{8} \times 3\frac{3}{5}$    7) $1\frac{7}{8} + 4\frac{1}{4}$    12) $\frac{5}{8} \times 4\frac{2}{3}$    17) $1\frac{1}{8} - \frac{3}{5}$

3) $1\frac{2}{3} \div 2\frac{2}{9}$    8) $4\frac{1}{3} - \frac{5}{6}$    13) $3\frac{1}{5} \div \frac{14}{15}$    18) $3\frac{1}{5} \times 1\frac{1}{4}$

4) $2\frac{5}{6} - \frac{1}{4}$    9) $2\frac{3}{4} \times 3$    14) $6 - 2\frac{2}{9}$    19) $2\frac{1}{2} + \frac{5}{8}$

5) $1\frac{5}{7} \times 2\frac{5}{8}$    10) $3\frac{2}{5} + 1\frac{1}{4}$    15) $2\frac{1}{3} + 1\frac{3}{5}$    20) $4\frac{1}{2} \div 1\frac{7}{8}$

**b**

1) $\left(\frac{1}{4} + \frac{1}{3}\right) \times \frac{4}{5}$      6) $1\frac{1}{20} \div \left(1\frac{1}{2} + 1\frac{1}{5}\right)$

2) $3\frac{2}{5} \div \left(2\frac{1}{2} + \frac{1}{3}\right)$      7) $\left(4\frac{1}{2} - 1\frac{3}{4}\right) \div 7\frac{1}{3}$

3) $\left(1\frac{1}{2} + 2\frac{2}{3}\right) \times 1\frac{1}{15}$      8) $3\frac{1}{7} \div 1\frac{3}{8} + \frac{1}{2}$

4) $1\frac{1}{10} \times \left(\frac{3}{4} - \frac{1}{3}\right)$      9) $4\frac{1}{6} \times \left(\frac{7}{8} - \frac{4}{5}\right)$

5) $3\frac{1}{3} - \left(\frac{5}{6} + 2\frac{1}{2}\right)$      10) $\left(\frac{3}{5} + 1\frac{1}{2}\right) \times 3$

**c**

1) $\left(1\frac{1}{6} - \frac{5}{9}\right) \div 1\frac{2}{3}$      7) $\dfrac{\frac{2}{3} - \frac{1}{5}}{\frac{11}{20} + 2\frac{1}{4}}$

2) $6\frac{2}{3} \times \left(1\frac{5}{8} - \frac{4}{5}\right)$

3) $\left(4\frac{5}{6} + 2\frac{1}{2}\right) \times 4\frac{1}{2}$      8) $\dfrac{\frac{1}{7} + \frac{1}{4}}{3\frac{3}{10}}$

4) $3\frac{7}{8} \div \left(4\frac{4}{9} + 1\frac{7}{12}\right)$

5) $\left(3\frac{5}{6} + 1\frac{1}{2}\right) \times \left(1\frac{1}{6} - \frac{3}{4}\right)$      9) $\dfrac{2\frac{4}{5} \div 3\frac{1}{2}}{\frac{1}{3} \times 1\frac{2}{5}}$

6) $\dfrac{1\frac{1}{2} + 2\frac{1}{10}}{3\frac{3}{5}}$      10) $\dfrac{2\frac{5}{8}}{2\frac{1}{2} - 1\frac{1}{3}}$

**d**

1) Multiply by $1\frac{7}{8}$ the sum of $1\frac{1}{5}$ and $2\frac{2}{3}$

2) Add $1\frac{3}{4}$ to the product of $2\frac{1}{4}$ and $1\frac{5}{6}$

3) Subtract $\frac{3}{4}$ from the sum of $\frac{7}{10}$ and $1\frac{3}{5}$

4) Multiply by $1\frac{4}{5}$ the difference between $2\frac{1}{4}$ and $\frac{7}{12}$

5) From the product of $5\frac{1}{3}$ and $\frac{5}{8}$ subtract $3\frac{1}{3}$

6) Divide by $5\frac{1}{5}$ the sum of $1\frac{1}{5}$ and $\frac{3}{4}$

7) Add $\frac{1}{2}$ to the product of $\frac{4}{9}$ and $3\frac{3}{5}$

8) Multiply the sum of $4\frac{1}{2}$ and $5\frac{3}{10}$ by $1\frac{3}{7}$

9) Divide the difference between $3\frac{2}{5}$ and $\frac{2}{3}$ by $5\frac{1}{8}$

10) Subtract $\frac{5}{6}$ from the product of $1\frac{7}{8}$ and $\frac{4}{5}$

# A CHANGING FRACTIONS TO DECIMALS

e.g. $\frac{3}{4}$

*1) Make the top (numerator)
   look like a decimal by
   writing .0 after it.

$$\frac{3 \cdot 0}{4}$$

*2) Divide the top (numerator)
   by the bottom (denominator)
   Add extra noughts if necessary

$$\begin{array}{r} .75 \\ 4\overline{)3 \cdot 0^2 0} \end{array}$$

$$\frac{3}{4} = 0 \cdot 75$$

**Some more examples**

| $\frac{1}{8}$ | $\frac{2}{5}$ | $\frac{11}{16}$ |
|---|---|---|
| $\frac{1 \cdot 0}{8}$ | $\frac{2 \cdot 0}{5}$ | $\frac{11 \cdot 0}{16}$ |
| $\begin{array}{r}.125\\8\overline{)1 \cdot 0\,00}\end{array}$ | $\begin{array}{r}.4\\5\overline{)2 \cdot 0}\end{array}$ | $\begin{array}{r}.6875\\16\overline{)11 \cdot 0\,000}\end{array}$ |
| $\frac{1}{8} = 0 \cdot 125$ | $\frac{2}{5} = 0 \cdot 4$ | $\frac{11}{16} = 0 \cdot 6875$ |

# B

Whole numbers STAY THE SAME    e.g. $2\frac{4}{5}$

Be careful not to forget the
whole numbers

$$2 \cdot \frac{4 \cdot 0}{5}$$

$$2 \qquad \begin{array}{r} .8 \\ 5\overline{)4 \cdot 0} \end{array}$$

$$2\frac{4}{5} = 2 \cdot 8$$

# C

Some fractions become RECURRING DECIMALS

e.g. $\frac{8}{9}$

$$\frac{8 \cdot 0}{9}$$

$$\begin{array}{r} .888 \text{ etc.} \\ 9\overline{)8 \cdot 000} \end{array}$$

$$\frac{8}{9} = 0 \cdot \dot{8}$$

e.g. $\frac{6}{11}$

$$\frac{6 \cdot 0}{11}$$

$$\begin{array}{r} .5454 \text{ etc.} \\ 11\overline{)6 \cdot 0\,000} \end{array}$$

$$\frac{6}{11} = 0 \cdot \dot{5}\dot{4}$$

## a

Change these fractions into decimals

1) $\frac{1}{4}$   6) $\frac{9}{20}$   11) $\frac{5}{16}$   16) $\frac{4}{5}$

2) $\frac{2}{5}$   7) $\frac{1}{2}$   12) $\frac{7}{10}$   17) $\frac{33}{40}$

3) $\frac{3}{8}$   8) $\frac{3}{10}$   13) $\frac{5}{8}$   18) $\frac{7}{25}$

4) $\frac{9}{10}$   9) $\frac{7}{16}$   14) $\frac{1}{5}$   19) $\frac{1}{10}$

5) $\frac{3}{5}$   10) $\frac{9}{25}$   15) $\frac{17}{20}$   20) $\frac{7}{8}$

## b

Change these fractions into decimals. Remember that
WHOLE NUMBERS STAY THE SAME

1) $2\frac{1}{8}$   6) $6\frac{3}{4}$   11) $3\frac{7}{8}$   16) $\frac{9}{40}$

2) $4\frac{9}{10}$   7) $\frac{39}{50}$   12) $1\frac{7}{10}$   17) $2\frac{2}{5}$

3) $3\frac{4}{5}$   8) $1\frac{5}{8}$   13) $5\frac{1}{4}$   18) $\frac{3}{20}$

4) $\frac{11}{25}$   9) $4\frac{1}{5}$   14) $8\frac{7}{10}$   19) $2\frac{1}{16}$

5) $12\frac{1}{2}$   10) $\frac{9}{16}$   15) $\frac{3}{25}$   20) $7\frac{3}{5}$

## c

Change these fractions into recurring decimals

1) $\frac{1}{9}$   6) $2\frac{2}{9}$   11) $\frac{7}{15}$   16) $1\frac{8}{11}$

2) $\frac{2}{3}$   7) $\frac{5}{12}$   12) $\frac{10}{11}$   17) $\frac{4}{15}$

3) $\frac{5}{6}$   8) $2\frac{1}{11}$   13) $5\frac{1}{6}$   18) $4\frac{3}{7}$

4) $\frac{4}{11}$   9) $1\frac{1}{3}$   14) $\frac{5}{18}$   19) $5\frac{2}{3}$

5) $\frac{7}{12}$   10) $\frac{11}{30}$   15) $\frac{1}{7}$   20) $\frac{4}{13}$

## d

Change these fractions into decimals. Some will be
recurring.

1) $1\frac{3}{10}$   6) $\frac{15}{16}$   11) $5\frac{9}{10}$   16) $\frac{69}{100}$

2) $2\frac{1}{4}$   7) $9\frac{3}{4}$   12) $23\frac{1}{2}$   17) $\frac{19}{20}$

3) $3\frac{2}{3}$   8) $4\frac{5}{6}$   13) $\frac{6}{7}$   18) $1\frac{8}{9}$

4) $\frac{5}{9}$   9) $\frac{21}{25}$   14) $1\frac{3}{8}$   19) $\frac{11}{12}$

5) $2\frac{4}{5}$   10) $6\frac{1}{5}$   15) $\frac{2}{15}$   20) $8\frac{1}{8}$

# CHANGING DECIMALS TO FRACTIONS

e.g.     0.65

*1) Make into a WHOLE NUMBER
by multiplying (in this case                    65
× 100)

*2) Put this over the number                   $\dfrac{65}{100}$
you have multiplied by

*3) Cancel as far as you can          $\dfrac{\cancel{65}^{13}}{\cancel{100}_{20}} = \dfrac{13}{20}$

---

**Some more examples**

| 0.8 | 0.46 | 0.125 |
|---|---|---|
| $\dfrac{8}{10}$ | $\dfrac{46}{100}$ | $\dfrac{125}{1000}$ |
| $\dfrac{\cancel{8}^{4}}{\cancel{10}_{5}}$ | $\dfrac{\cancel{46}^{23}}{\cancel{100}_{50}}$ | $\dfrac{\cancel{125}^{1}}{\cancel{1000}_{8}}$ |
| $\dfrac{4}{5}$ | $\dfrac{23}{50}$ | $\dfrac{1}{8}$ |

---

## REMEMBER

If decimal has ONE decimal place (e.g. 0.7) put over 10 ( $\frac{7}{10}$ )

If decimal has TWO decimal places (e.g. 0.21) put over 100 ( $\frac{21}{100}$ )

If decimal has THREE decimal places (e.g. 0.433)
put over 1000 ( $\frac{433}{1000}$ )

---

Whole numbers STAY THE SAME          e.g.    3.4

Be careful not to forget the whole numbers

$$3\dfrac{\cancel{4}^{2}}{\cancel{10}_{5}}$$

$$3\dfrac{2}{5}$$

**a** Change these decimals into fractions

| | | | |
|---|---|---|---|
| 1) 0.2 | 6) 0.375 | 11) 0.38 | 16) 0.775 |
| 2) 0.56 | 7) 0.88 | 12) 0.001 | 17) 0.48 |
| 3) 0.7 | 8) 0.975 | 13) 0.9 | 18) 0.15 |
| 4) 0.105 | 9) 0.04 | 14) 0.24 | 19) 0.6 |
| 5) 0.35 | 10) 0.13 | 15) 0.75 | 20) 0.78 |

**b** Express as fractions

| | | | |
|---|---|---|---|
| 1) 0.25 | 6) 0.08 | 11) 0.22 | 16) 0.85 |
| 2) 0.112 | 7) 0.625 | 12) 0.002 | 17) 0.1 |
| 3) 0.44 | 8) 0.3 | 13) 0.05 | 18) 0.675 |
| 4) 0.4 | 9) 0.58 | 14) 0.432 | 19) 0.0006 |
| 5) 0.075 | 10) 0.01 | 15) 0.5 | 20) 0.45 |

**c** Change these decimals into fractions.
Remember that WHOLE NUMBERS STAY THE SAME

| | | | |
|---|---|---|---|
| 1) 0.96 | 6) 1.95 | 11) 0.875 | 16) 0.416 |
| 2) 3.75 | 7) 2.64 | 12) 1.52 | 17) 2.36 |
| 3) 1.4 | 8) 3.8 | 13) 0.0625 | 18) 3.275 |
| 4) 0.82 | 9) 0.55 | 14) 4.5 | 19) 1.02 |
| 5) 4.125 | 10) 6.16 | 15) 0.12 | 20) 8.7 |

**d** Express as fractions

| | | | |
|---|---|---|---|
| 1) 5.06 | 6) 0.315 | 11) 0.504 | 16) 4.725 |
| 2) 1.92 | 7) 1.32 | 12) 4.28 | 17) 0.008 |
| 3) 0.425 | 8) 0.8875 | 13) 3.68 | 18) 0.84 |
| 4) 7.9 | 9) 3.2 | 14) 5.475 | 19) 0.7575 |
| 5) 0.95 | 10) 8.72 | 15) 14.6 | 20) 12.25 |

# A ARRANGING DECIMALS IN ORDER OF SIZE

e.g. Arrange 2.645, 2.189, 3.7 in order of size, starting with the largest.

*1) Set out in columns

$\begin{array}{r} 2.645 \\ 2.189 \\ 3.7 \end{array}$

*2) Look at largest column

$\boxed{2}.645$
$\boxed{2}.189$
$\boxed{3}.7$

3 is the largest in this column, so 3.7 is the largest

The others are both 2, so

*3) Look at the next column

$2.\boxed{6}45$
$2.\boxed{1}89$

6 is larger than 1, so 2.645 is next. The order is 3.7, 2.645, 2.189.

---

# B ARRANGING FRACTIONS IN ORDER OF SIZE

e.g. Arrange $\frac{1}{4}$, $\frac{5}{16}$, $\frac{6}{25}$, $\frac{3}{11}$ in order of size starting with the largest.

*1) Change to DECIMALS (see page 50) and set out in columns

$\frac{1}{4} = 0.25$
$\frac{5}{16} = 0.3125$
$\frac{6}{25} = 0.24$
$\frac{3}{11} = 0.27272$

*2) In largest column, every figure is 0, so look at next column

$0.\boxed{2}5$
$0.\boxed{3}125$
$0.\boxed{2}4$
$0.\boxed{2}7272$

3 is larger than 2, so 0.3125 is largest. The others are all 2, so

*3) Look at next column.
7 is largest of these
5 is next
4 is next

$0.2\boxed{5}$
$0.2\boxed{4}$
$0.2\boxed{7}272$

The order is 0.3125, 0.27272, 0.25, 0.24

or $\frac{5}{16}$, $\frac{3}{11}$, $\frac{1}{4}$, $\frac{6}{25}$

## a

Arrange the numbers in each of these groups in order
of size, starting with the LARGEST

1) 5.3, 4.2, 6.0, 3.1
2) 2.4, 1.8, 2.6, 2.3
3) 0.76, 1.3, 0.81
4) 19.2, 18.56, 20.8, 19.7
5) 4.35, 4.32, 4.29. 4.19
6) 20.79, 35.6, 31.23, 48.7
7) 13.25, 21.08, 13.27, 12.92
8) 0.72, 0.78, 0.27

9) 2.58, 2.78, 2.5, 2.87
10) 8.02, 7.36, 7.19, 7.33
11) 0.45, 0.4, 0.54, 0.48, 0.5
12) 8.8, 8.08, 0.88, 8.808
13) 6.37, 6.39, 6.375, 6.4
14) 0.193, 0.182, 0.181, 0.191, 0.187
15) 0.5454, 0.532, 0.545, 0.5326

## b

Arrange the fractions in each of these groups in order of size
starting with the LARGEST

1) $\frac{3}{4}$, $\frac{4}{5}$, $\frac{1}{10}$
2) $\frac{2}{3}$, $\frac{7}{10}$, $\frac{1}{2}$
3) $\frac{1}{5}$, $\frac{1}{8}$, $\frac{3}{10}$
4) $\frac{3}{20}$, $\frac{2}{9}$, $\frac{1}{5}$
5) $\frac{7}{9}$, $\frac{5}{6}$, $\frac{9}{10}$
6) $\frac{6}{11}$, $\frac{5}{8}$, $\frac{3}{5}$, $\frac{1}{2}$
7) $\frac{3}{7}$, $\frac{2}{5}$, $\frac{1}{2}$, $\frac{9}{20}$

8) $\frac{9}{10}$, $\frac{21}{25}$, $\frac{17}{20}$
9) $\frac{9}{16}$, $\frac{11}{20}$, $\frac{13}{25}$
10) $\frac{17}{50}$, $\frac{3}{8}$, $\frac{1}{3}$, $\frac{7}{20}$
11) $\frac{3}{20}$, $\frac{2}{11}$, $\frac{1}{8}$
12) $\frac{8}{9}$, $\frac{22}{25}$, $\frac{7}{8}$
13) $\frac{5}{9}$, $\frac{3}{5}$, $\frac{12}{25}$, $\frac{4}{7}$
14) $\frac{7}{10}$, $\frac{7}{9}$, $\frac{3}{4}$, $\frac{18}{25}$

15) $1\frac{1}{2}$, $2\frac{1}{4}$, $\frac{3}{8}$, $1\frac{3}{5}$
16) $\frac{4}{5}$, $\frac{17}{20}$, $\frac{6}{7}$
17) $\frac{23}{25}$, $\frac{9}{10}$, $\frac{15}{16}$
18) $\frac{1}{2}$, $\frac{4}{7}$, $\frac{8}{15}$, $\frac{7}{12}$
19) $\frac{5}{18}$, $\frac{3}{11}$, $\frac{11}{40}$
20) $\frac{5}{12}$, $\frac{4}{9}$, $\frac{3}{8}$, $\frac{9}{20}$

## c

Arrange the numbers in each of these groups in order of size
starting with the SMALLEST

1) $\frac{3}{5}$, $\frac{2}{3}$, $\frac{7}{11}$, $\frac{13}{20}$
2) $\frac{11}{16}$, $\frac{17}{25}$, $\frac{7}{10}$
3) 1.32, 1.23, 1.3, 1.26
4) $\frac{17}{20}$, $\frac{6}{7}$, $\frac{11}{13}$
5) $\frac{1}{6}$, $\frac{4}{25}$, 0.155, $\frac{3}{20}$
6) 921, 1219, 219, 2191
7) $4\frac{5}{9}$, $4.59$, $4\frac{3}{5}$, $4.53$
8) $\frac{4}{11}$, $\frac{3}{8}$, 0.31, $\frac{1}{3}$

9) 11000, 1010, 10101, 1100
10) $\frac{10}{13}$, $\frac{3}{4}$, $\frac{5}{7}$
11) 0.032, 0.0302, 0.0032, 0.3
12) $\frac{8}{9}$, $\frac{9}{11}$, $\frac{13}{16}$
13) 0.085, $\frac{1}{12}$, 0.084
14) 53.6999, 53.694, 53.6995, 53.7
15) $\frac{3}{8}$, $\frac{7}{18}$, $\frac{4}{11}$, $\frac{9}{25}$, $\frac{5}{13}$

#  CHANGING FRACTIONS TO PERCENTAGES (%)   e.g.   $\frac{3}{4}$

*Multiply by 100

$$\frac{3}{4} \times \frac{100}{1}$$

Do not forget to write
  the % sign

$$_1\frac{3}{\cancel{4}} \times \frac{\cancel{100}^{25}}{1}$$

$$75\%$$

**Other examples**

$$\frac{1}{8} \qquad\qquad 1\frac{4}{5} \qquad\qquad \frac{4}{9}$$

$$_2\frac{1}{\cancel{8}} \times \frac{\cancel{100}^{25}}{1} \qquad _1\frac{9}{\cancel{5}} \times \frac{\cancel{100}^{20}}{1} \qquad \frac{4}{9} \times \frac{100}{1}$$

$$\frac{25}{2} \qquad\qquad \frac{180}{1} \qquad\qquad \frac{400}{9}$$

$$12\frac{1}{2}\% \qquad\qquad 180\% \qquad\qquad 44\frac{4}{9}\%$$

# B CHANGING DECIMALS TO PERCENTAGES (%)   e.g.   0.54

* Multiply by 100

$$0.54 \times 100$$

Do not forget to write
  the % sign

$$54\%$$

**Other examples**

$$0.7 \qquad\qquad 0.925 \qquad\qquad 1.43$$

$$0.7 \times 100 \qquad 0.925 \times 100 \qquad 1.43 \times 100$$

$$70\% \qquad\qquad 92.5\% \qquad\qquad 143\%$$

# C EXPRESSING A NUMBER AS A PERCENTAGE OF ANOTHER NUMBER

e.g.   Express 4 as a percentage of 15

*1) Write the first number OVER the
    second number as a fraction

$$\frac{4}{15}$$

*2) Multiply by 100

$$_3\frac{4}{\cancel{15}} \times \frac{\cancel{100}^{20}}{1}$$

$$\frac{80}{3}$$

$$26\tfrac{2}{3}\%$$

**a** Write these fractions as percentages

1) $\frac{2}{5}$    6) $\frac{21}{25}$    11) $\frac{1}{2}$    16) $3\frac{7}{10}$

2) $\frac{37}{100}$    7) $\frac{3}{8}$    12) $\frac{14}{15}$    17) $\frac{9}{25}$

3) $\frac{1}{4}$    8) $\frac{13}{20}$    13) $1\frac{1}{20}$    18) $\frac{27}{40}$

4) $\frac{7}{20}$    9) $\frac{5}{12}$    14) $\frac{5}{8}$    19) $1\frac{1}{10}$

5) $\frac{1}{3}$    10) $\frac{9}{10}$    15) $2\frac{3}{5}$    20) $\frac{99}{100}$

**b** Write these decimals as percentages

1) 0.6    6) 0.98    11) 1.3    16) 0.274

2) 0.25    7) 0.2    12) 0.785    17) 1.59

3) 0.875    8) 0.1325    13) 0.86    18) 0.001

4) 0.39    9) 0.44    14) 0.52    19) 1.04

5) 0.02    10) 0.13    15) 2.15    20) 0.9

**c**
1) Express 3 as a percentage of 10
2) Express 41 as a percentage of 50
3) Express 17 as a percentage of 20
4) Express 8 as a percentage of 16
5) Express 1 as a percentage of 25
6) Express 35 as a percentage of 56
7) Express 15 as a percentage of 75
8) Express 10½ as a percentage of 14
9) Express 464 as a percentage of 400
10) Express 162 as a percentage of 720

**d**
1) John scored 16 marks out of 20. What percentage was this?
2) Write £9 as a percentage of £15.
3) Out of 240 marbles, 156 were red. What percentage were red?
4) Express 3.5 as a percentage of 70
5) There were 720 children in a crowd of 1600. What percentage of the crowd were children?
6) What is 84 as a percentage of 90?
7) Of 175 passengers in an airliner, 56 were Americans. What percentage were Americans?
8) In a certain book, 18 of the 25 pictures are in colour. What percentage are in colour?
9) Out of 25 trains arriving at a station, 8 were late. What percentage of the trains were NOT late?
10) Of a class of 20 pupils, 17 were present. What percentage were absent?

56

## A CHANGING PERCENTAGES TO FRACTIONS
e.g.  68%

*1)  Write the percentage OVER 100

$$\frac{68}{100}$$

*2)  Cancel as far as you can

$$\frac{\cancel{68}^{17}}{\cancel{100}_{25}}$$

$$\frac{17}{25}$$

## B CHANGING FRACTION PERCENTAGES TO FRACTIONS
e.g.  27½%

*1)  Write the percentage OVER 100

$$\frac{27\frac{1}{2}}{100}$$

*2)  Multiply top and bottom by the denominator of the fraction.

$$\frac{27\frac{1}{2}\times2}{100\times2}=\frac{55}{200}$$

*3)  Cancel as far as you can

$$\frac{\cancel{55}^{11}}{\cancel{200}_{40}}$$

$$\frac{11}{40}$$

e.g. (2)    11¼%

$$\frac{11\frac{1}{4}}{100}$$

$$\frac{11\frac{1}{4}\times4}{100\times4}=\frac{45}{400}$$

$$\frac{\cancel{45}}{\cancel{400}}=\frac{9}{80}$$

e.g. (3)    16⅔%

$$\frac{16\frac{2}{3}}{100}$$

$$\frac{16\frac{2}{3}\times3}{100\times3}=\frac{50}{300}$$

$$\frac{\cancel{50}}{\cancel{300}}=\frac{1}{6}$$

## C CHANGING PERCENTAGES TO DECIMALS
e.g. 72%

*Divide by 100 (see page 14)

$$72\div100$$
$$0\cdot72$$

If the percentage contains a fraction, change it all to a decimal, and then divide by 100

**a** Change these percentages to fractions

| | | | |
|---|---|---|---|
| 1) 20% | 6) 29% | 11) 24% | 16) 76% |
| 2) 75% | 7) 60% | 12) 2% | 17) 99% |
| 3) 34% | 8) 85% | 13) 44% | 18) 7½% |
| 4) 90% | 9) 4% | 14) 10% | 19) 50% |
| 5) 15% | 10) 81% | 15) 35% | 20) 65% |

**b** Express as fractions

| | | | |
|---|---|---|---|
| 1) 25% | 6) 31¼% | 11) 73⅓% | 16) 50⅖% |
| 2) 1% | 7) 28% | 12) 5% | 17) 12% |
| 3) 45% | 8) 62½% | 13) 77% | 18) 70% |
| 4) 80% | 9) 33⅓% | 14) 47½% | 19) 87½% |
| 5) 22½% | 10) 9% | 15) 100% | 20) 68¾% |

**c** Write these percentages as fractions. If your answer is an IMPROPER (top-heavy) fraction, change it to a mixed number — see page 26

| | | | |
|---|---|---|---|
| 1) 72% | 6) 91⅔% | 11) 83⅓% | 16) 48% |
| 2) 140% | 7) 275% | 12) ½% | 17) 12½% |
| 3) 53⅓% | 8) 30% | 13) 284% | 18) 58¾% |
| 4) 82½% | 9) 155% | 14) 76⅔% | 19) 320% |
| 5) 95% | 10) 37½% | 15) 17½% | 20) 58⅓% |

**d** Write these percentages as decimals

| | | | |
|---|---|---|---|
| 1) 62% | 6) 105% | 11) 6.5% | 16) 38.9% |
| 2) 79% | 7) 88% | 12) 140% | 17) 18¼% |
| 3) 18% | 8) 43.7% | 13) 17½% | 18) 222% |
| 4) 54% | 9) 98% | 14) 59.75% | 19) 50% |
| 5) 3% | 10) 13% | 15) 1% | 20) 27% |

# FINDING x% OF A NUMBER

e.g.   32% of 67

*1) Write again, with the percentage as a fraction over 100
Remember OF means ×

$$\frac{32}{100} \times \frac{67}{1}$$

*2) Work out. It is usually better to LEAVE 100 at the bottom rather than cancelling

$$\frac{32 \times 67}{100 \times 1} = \frac{2144}{100}$$

*3) Divide top by bottom

$$2144 \div 100$$
$$21.44$$

---

e.g.   (2)   6% of 91

$$\frac{6}{100} \times \frac{91}{1}$$

$$\frac{546}{100}$$

$$5.46$$

e.g.   (3)   75% of £365

$$\frac{75}{100} \times \frac{365}{1}$$

$$\frac{27375}{100}$$

$$£273.75$$

---

 # FINDING x% OF NUMBERS WITH FRACTIONS

*These can be done just like the ones at the top of the page, but it sometimes helps to multiply top and bottom first by the same number

e.g.   (1)   $17\frac{1}{2}$ % of £54

Multiply top and bottom by 2

$$\frac{17\frac{1}{2}}{100} \times \frac{54}{1}$$

$$\frac{35}{200} \times \frac{54}{1}$$

Then cancel by 2 if possible

$$\frac{35}{200_{100}} \times \frac{\overset{27}{54}}{1}$$

$$\frac{945}{100}$$

$$£9.45$$

e.g.   (2)   56% of $7\frac{1}{4}$

Multiply top and bottom by 4

$$\frac{56}{100} \times \frac{7\frac{1}{4}}{1}$$

$$\frac{56}{100} \times \frac{29}{4}$$

Then cancel by 4 if possible

$$\frac{\overset{14}{56}}{100} \times \frac{29}{\underset{1}{4}}$$

$$\frac{406}{100}$$

$$4.06$$

**a**

1) 4% of 250
2) 7% of 72
3) 22% of 675
4) 15% of 200
5) 90% of 36

6) 10% of 85
7) 37% of 600
8) 110% of 6
9) 9% of 1230
10) 2.5% of 84

11) 58% of 58
12) 30% of 2
13) 72% of 62.5
14) 1% of 93
15) 88% of 320

**b**

1) 42% of 150
2) 12½% of 64
3) 3% of 2500
4) 8½% of 196
5) 120% of 24

6) 325% of 20
7) 5⅓% of 714
8) 17% of 43
9) 5% of 666
10) 42% of 87½

11) 10½% of 4350
12) 65% of 118
13) 2¼% of 960
14) 38% of 7
15) 6⅔% of 45

**c**

Try these. Remember to put the correct units in your answer, e.g. if question is in £, so is answer (35% of £80 = £28); if question is in metres, so is answer (9% of 175 metres = 15.75 metres)

1) 25% of £144
2) 7% of 360m
3) 80% of 45p
4) 55% of 60 km
5) 18% of 28 grams
6) 92% of 500 metres
7) 35% of £95
8) 4½% of 300 ml

9) 10% of 39.46 litres
10) 77% of 215 mm
11) 16¼% of 384 kg
12) 11.5% of £6
13) 48% of 130 tonnes
14) 66⅔% of 12 ha
15) 1½% of £2000

**d**

1) 6% of 51 cm
2) 250% of £8
3) 18.5% of 420
4) 61% of 43g
5) 33⅓% of 5685 tonnes
6) 21% of 7⅔
7) 104% of 450 litres
8) 82% of $775

9) 45% of 60 miles
10) 0.5% of 0.5 mg
11) 29% of 67
12) 90% of 4 ml
13) 12½% of £8500
14) 53% of 14.5
15) 9¼% of £156

# A TO INCREASE OR DECREASE BY PERCENTAGE

e.g.   INCREASE (make larger)   35 by 40%

Increase is 40% of 35 $= \frac{40}{100} \times \frac{35}{1} = 14$

so answer is  35 + 14   =   49

e.g.   DECREASE (make smaller)   £125 by 6%

Decrease is 6% of 125   $= \frac{6}{100} \times \frac{125}{1} = 7.5$

so answer is   125 − 7.5   =   £117.50

# B PERCENTAGE PROFIT AND LOSS

## Profit (or gain or increase)

Percentage profit $= \frac{\text{Profit}}{\text{Original amount}} \times \frac{100}{1}$

e.g.   Mrs Jones bought an antique vase for £120.  Later she sold it for £150.  What was her percentage profit?

The profit (extra amount she gained) was

150   −   120   =   £30

So **percentage profit** was $\frac{30}{120} \times \frac{100}{1}$   =   25%

## Loss (or decrease)

Percentage Loss $= \frac{\text{Loss}}{\text{Original amount}} \times \frac{100}{1}$

e.g.   Tom bought a car for £4000 and later sold it for £3300. What was his percentage loss?

The loss (amount that Tom lost) was

4000   −   3300   =   £700

so **percentage loss** was $\frac{700}{4000} \times \frac{100}{1}$ = $17\frac{1}{2}$ %

**a**

1) Increase 48 by 25%
2) Increase 130 by 10%
3) Decrease 500 by 35%
4) Increase 60 by 5%
5) Decrease 250 by 18%
6) Decrease 24 by 12½%
7) Increase 365 by 140%
8) Decrease 72 by 75%

9) Increase £185 by 20%
10) Decrease 64 by 3%
11) Increase 752 by 22½%
12) Decrease £245 by 26%
13) Decrease 9 by 60%
14) Increase 360 by 15%
15) Increase £21 by 33⅓%

---

**b**

1) John bought a new bicycle for £120. Later he sold it for £90. What was the percentage loss?

2) Mrs Morgan's shop sold cans of cola at 21p each. The cans of cola cost Mrs Morgan 12p each. What percentage profit did she make?

3) A girl put £250 in a bank account. After a year she received £275. What was her percentage gain?

4) What is the percentage profit if a motorbike is bought for £625 and sold for £725?

5) A man bought a horse for £500 and later sold it for £2250. What percentage profit did he make?

6) Nick added 2 new cars to his collection of 40 models. What was the percentage increase in his collection?

7) A cottage was bought for £36000 and sold for £43200. What was the percentage profit?

8) Fiona bought a bracelet for £12.50 and sold it for £10.25. What was her percentage loss?

9) Derek's Transport bought a truck for £8000 and later sold it for £7400. What was the percentage loss?

10) Last year a club had 96 members. This year it has 108. What was the percentage increase in membership?

# SOME EXTRA QUESTIONS

1) 1428.57 × 0.7

2) Write 1.45 as a fraction in its lowest terms

3) Divide by 0.9 the sum of 3.3 and 0.84

4) $2\frac{5}{8} \times \frac{5}{7} \div 1\frac{1}{2}$

5) Arrange in order of size, starting with largest
   9.809, 9.908, 9.089, 9.9, 9.890

6) $1\frac{5}{9} \div (1\frac{1}{6} + 1\frac{3}{4})$

7) A man bought a stamp collection for £350 and sold it later for £420. What was the percentage profit?

8) Express $4\frac{3}{16}$ as a decimal

9) What is the sum of 13.13, 9.59 and 7.28?

10) Jane bought a cake. Sally ate $\frac{1}{4}$ of it and Jane ate $\frac{1}{3}$ of it. What fraction of the cake had they eaten?

---

11) $4\frac{1}{5} \times 4\frac{1}{6} + 4\frac{5}{6}$

12) Andrew bought a pair of training shoes at £13.95 a pair, a plastic football at £2.95 and a magazine at 65p. How much did he spend altogether?

13) Express $\frac{37}{40}$ as a percentage

14) Write as a fraction 7.32

15) From the product of 6.5 and 3.8 subtract 9.55

16) Divide by $8\frac{1}{4}$ the difference between $8\frac{1}{2}$ and $1\frac{5}{8}$

17) Find 61% of £625

18) 0.775 + 0.099 − 0.208

19) Jeremy drank $\frac{4}{5}$ of $\frac{3}{4}$ of $\frac{5}{6}$ of the coffee in his flask. What fraction of the coffee was still left?

20) Divide 0.455 by 1.3 and express your answer as a fraction in its lowest terms

---

21) Express 56% as a fraction in its lowest terms

22) $2\frac{1}{6} + 1\frac{3}{4} - 3\frac{2}{3}$

23) Find the product of 0.026 and 935

24) Kate planned to spend the evening sticking her holiday photographs in an album. She had 45 photographs altogether but by supper time she had stuck in only 36. What fraction of the photographs had she stuck in?

25) Which is the smallest of $\frac{1}{6}$, $\frac{2}{15}$ and $\frac{3}{20}$ ?

26) $(1.79 + 1.168) \div 3.4$

27) For helping the farmer, Giles and Paul were given £18 to share between them. As Giles had worked harder than Paul, they both agreed that Giles should have $\frac{7}{12}$ of the money and Paul should have the rest of it. How much money did Paul have?

28) Write $3\frac{7}{11}$ as a recurring decimal

29) How much water would there be in 19 containers if each container held 4.55 litres of water?

30) Find 37 ½ % of 56 kilograms

---

31) $11 - 3.7 - 1.92$

32) Find the product of $\frac{3}{8}$ and $7\frac{1}{3}$ and express the answer as a decimal

33) Increase 450 by 14%

34) Find the total cost of 4 tins of beans at 26p each, 3 jars of jam at 37p each and a packet of cornflakes at 39p

35) What is $\frac{2}{3}$ of $\frac{7}{8}$ of 552?

36) Gary is $10\frac{1}{2}$ years old and his Uncle Bob is 28. Express Gary's age as a fraction of Uncle Bob's age.

37) Karen bought a camera in the summer holidays for £25. At the end of the winter term she sold it to a friend for £19. What was the percentage loss?

38) $\dfrac{5\frac{5}{8}}{4\frac{1}{6}}$

39) Multiply the sum of 8.53 and 3.97 by 0.72

40) $(4\frac{1}{2} - 2\frac{4}{7}) \times (1\frac{1}{2} + 2\frac{7}{9})$

41) A team played 20 matches and won 14 of them. The other matches were all lost. What percentage of their matches did they LOSE?

42) $\frac{5}{8} \times (5\frac{1}{3} - 1\frac{3}{5})$

43) Express 98 as a percentage of 112

44) Multiply by 0.15 the difference between 0.9 and 0.077

45) $\dfrac{3\frac{2}{3} + 1\frac{5}{6}}{5\frac{4}{5} - 2\frac{1}{2}}$

46) A firm pays all its 16 workers the same wage. Each week the firm pays £1916 wages. How much does each worker receive each week?

47) Arrange in order of size, starting with largest
$$\frac{8}{11}, \quad \frac{3}{4}, \quad \frac{18}{25}, \quad \frac{11}{15}$$

48) Decrease 16 by 15%

49) Patrick had a collection of 300 marbles. He gave $\frac{5}{12}$ of the collection to his brother Harry and $\frac{3}{10}$ of the collection to his friend James. How many marbles did he give away altogether?

50) Write $\frac{7}{18}$ as a decimal